John Dalton
Critical Assessments
of His Life and Science

HARVARD MONOGRAPHS IN THE HISTORY OF SCIENCE

HARVARD MONOGRAPHS IN
THE HISTORY OF SCIENCE

Chinese Alchemy: Preliminary Studies by Nathan Sivin
Leonhard Rauwolf: Sixteenth-Century Physician, Botanist, and Traveler by Karl H. Dannenfeldt
Reflexes and Motor Integration: Sherrington's Concept of Integrative Action by Judith P. Swazey
Atoms and Powers: An Essay on Newtonian Matter-Theory and the Development of Chemistry by Arnold Thackray
The Astrological History of Māshā'allāh by E. S. Kennedy and David Pingree
Treatise of Man: René Descartes by Thomas Steele Hall
John Dalton: Critical Assessments of His Life and Science by Arnold Thackray

John Dalton. From an engraving of the 1814 portrait by Joseph Allen. (Courtesy of the Manchester Public Libraries.)

John Dalton

Critical Assessments
of His Life and Science

Arnold Thackray

Harvard University Press
Cambridge, Massachusetts
1972

To Sir Harold Hartley and I. Bernard Cohen
who encouraged these studies

Acknowledgements

It is a pleasure to indicate some of the many debts I have incurred in the course of this work. I owe especial gratitude to Professor I. Bernard Cohen for his generous encouragement, judicious suggestions, and wise advice. Together with Sir Harold Hartley he fostered my early interest in John Dalton and urged its continuance to this conclusion. I have also profited from the thoughtful help of many other colleagues and friends, especially Dr. Y. Elkana, Dr. W. V. Farrar, Dr. F. Greenaway, Dr. M. B. Hesse, Dr. D. M. Knight, Professor T. S. Kuhn, Professor E. Mendelsohn, Professor R. K. Merton, Mrs. E. Patterson, Professor R. E. Schofield, and Dr. W. A. Smeaton. Dr. W. B. Cannon and Mr. J. B. Morrell were kind enough to read through the entire manuscript, and I have benefited greatly from their critical comments. The enlightened support of the National Science Foundation has facilitated those continuing researches of which the present book is one early fruit.

For the opportunity to work in their archives and for assistance willingly given, I must severally thank Mr. John Dalton of Kerikeri, New Zealand; Mr. Thomas Hodgkin of The Mill, Ilmington, Warwickshire; and the librarians of: The American Philosophical Society; The Historical Society of Pennsylvania; The Universities of Durham, Edinburgh, Liverpool, Manchester, and Pennsylvania; Trinity College, Cambridge; Magdalen College,

Oxford; The National Library of Scotland; The British Museum; The Royal Society of London; The Royal Institution, London; The Science Museum, London; The Wellcome Historical Medical Library, London; The Society of Friends, London; The John Rylands Library, Manchester; The Manchester Literary and Philosophical Society; The Manchester Central Library; Manchester College, Oxford; Warrington Public Library; Kendal Public Library; Carlisle Public Library; The Cumberland and Westmorland Record Office, Carlisle; The Fitz Park Museum, Kendal; and the Kendal Meeting of the Society of Friends.

In quoting both manuscript and printed material, orthography and punctuation have been extensively and silently modernized. Contractions have likewise been expanded, but in no case has the original sense or word order been altered. Full bibliographical data on books mentioned within the main text are given in the concluding bibliographic essay. Publishers of twentieth-century works cited in the footnotes are given either in the bibliographic essay or in the first footnote citation of a work. All books referred to were published in London, except when otherwise noted. The *Memoirs and Proceedings of the Manchester Literary and Philosophical Society* are identified throughout by their familiar title of *Manchester Memoirs,* with volumes cited by their modern numbers. Separately issued *Proceedings* of the Society are referred to as such.

The essays that follow draw on, revise, and add considerably to material that first appeared in *Annals of Science, The British Journal for the History of Science, The Dictionary of Scientific Biography* (Article "John Dalton" in volume III, *Dictionary of Scientific Biography.* Copyright © 1971 American Council of Learned Societies. By permission of Charles Scribner's Sons), *History of Science, Isis, Manchester Memoirs,* and the *Sources of Science.* I am grateful to their editors and proprietors for appropriate permissions.

Last but by no means least I gladly acknowledge the cheerful secretarial aid of Mrs. Marthenia Perrin, Miss Linda Polin, and Miss Betsy Shapiro, and the long-suffering care of Mrs. W. M.

Frohock and Mr. Joseph Elder of the Harvard University Press. Without their several contributions this monograph would still be but illegible notes in undecipherable script.

                                                                          Arnold Thackray

Primrose Hill, London
Christmas Eve, 1971

Contents

Illustrations

John Dalton

Critical Assessments
of His Life and Science

1. Introduction

The facts which I have
endeavoured to ascertain . . .
will excuse me for a momentary
indulgence of the ideas of
a visionary theorist.
                    John Dalton in 1793

Many pressing tasks confront historians of the scientific enterprise. One of the most varied and demanding in its content is to describe and assay some of those major figures whose lives not only possess the fascination of individual greatness but cast significant light on at least one period, country, or discipline. Those whose activities also reflect and illuminate fundamental transformations in the very structure of natural knowledge have an obvious priority. John Dalton thus presents both challenge and opportunity.

On the one hand, Dalton was a front-rank innovative thinker and experimenter. His fundamental contributions ranged widely. His crowning achievement was the enunciation of the chemical atomic theory. By its stress on the fundamental units of reaction, this theory focused attention on weight as *the* chemical parameter, and on structure and proportion as allied keys to understanding. It thus gave purpose and direction to chemical research throughout the nineteenth century. Dalton was also responsible for the first full description of color blindness (Daltonism), major advances in the physics of gases, and a variety of important meteorological speculations. His ideas not only help us to understand some of the research problems preoccupying British thinkers of the later eighteenth and early nineteenth centuries. They also shed light on the cognitive aspects of scientific change, on science as an empirical and conceptual undertaking.

1

On the other hand, Dalton was an archetypal "new man" of Industrial Revolution science, using his very considerable talents to help create and exploit the novel societal opportunities available to the natural philosopher in an urbanizing and industrializing culture. His activities thus tell us much about science as a social enterprise, about natural knowledge as a culturally bound group endeavor. John Dalton was a Protestant Dissenter of modest background, limited formal education, and severe plainness. Yet he came to know great public rewards. In later life he mixed freely among Manchester's industrial élite, commanded the presidency of a major and respected scientific organization for twenty-seven years, won international recognition and foreign honors, was presented at Court and granted a Government pension, in addition to receiving widespread acclaim, honorary degrees, and a Royal Medal. He lived to see his fellow citizens commission his portrait and his statue and was everywhere apotheosized as the dedicated man of science. All these things are reflections of how his lifetime encapsulated a fundamental transformation in the British pursuit of natural knowledge. The decades of the first Industrial Revolution witnessed a professionalizing reorganization in which the leisured, casual virtuoso was replaced by the remunerated, committed scientist. In old age Dalton thus came to be seen both as valiant precursor and as exemplary model for the new life of science. He did not fit either role as closely as contemporary commentators believed, which adds to the historical challenge presented by his life and work.

That a man of Dalton's abilities and achievements has exercised a continuing fascination upon historians is not surprising. The results of that fascination are catalogued in A. L. Smyth's *John Dalton. A Bibliography of Works by and about Him* (1966). Smyth lists no less than 116 articles on Dalton's life, and 161 on his work, in addition to twelve books devoted solely to him. The 1966 bicentenary of Dalton's birth was the signal for a fresh flurry of interest, of which the *Bibliography* was itself a portent. Since the bicentenary many articles and no less than three further books on Dalton have appeared. Clearly the man has not yet lost his appeal.

My own first interest was prompted by a desire to understand the origins of chemical atomic theory. I soon felt the challenge to weigh and sift the available evidence on a person given to deliberate deprecation of his early background, ill-served by careless Victorian biographers, and now apparently rendered almost inaccessible by the destruction of the main archive of his manuscripts (in a bombing raid on Manchester in 1940). The following essays display the results of my interest. Each chapter stands complete in itself, though their themes and contents are necessarily interwoven. Even when taken together, they do not pretend to offer a definitive statement on either John Dalton's life or his scientific work. Nor do they attempt to supplant the excellent popular biographies recently produced by Frank Greenaway and Elizabeth Patterson. They do, however, seek to show how much there is still to learn, on both factual and analytical levels, about a supposedly well-understood, and certainly much-studied, Industrial Revolution man of science.

To this end the essays that follow include a variety of important and previously unknown manuscripts and a selection of printed but neglected documents and syllabi. These new sources settle many points of interpretation, controverted over the years only because amateur (and, on occasion, professional) historians failed to blend imagination and analysis with a sufficient search for surviving and *available* records. The manuscripts utilized here have slowly accreted in some two dozen repositories on two continents. No doubt further items as yet unknown will gradually become available (certainly, unrecorded Dalton letters appear in dealers' hands from time to time). However, the information here brought to light should be sufficient both to destroy the myth that all worthwhile unpublished sources perished in the 1940 air-raid and to render unlikely significant future additions to our documentary knowledge. The present manuscripts include the very important syllabus of the 1807 Edinburgh lectures in which Dalton first displayed to the world the full power, range, and elegance of the chemical atomic theory; a later retrospective account of his early atomic weight studies; long-neglected Quaker archives which graphically display the unsuspected scientific riches of the education available in a north-country town; and seventy-three Dalton letters which offer many fresh insights into all phases of his life, while more than doubling the epistolary resources previously available.

I have chosen to print in full only a selection of the available manuscripts. My criteria were that the item in question be previously unknown and that it either provide new insights into Dalton's intellectual growth and achievement (especially as regards the chemical atomic theory), or that it help round out our picture of the life of a late Hanoverian natural philosopher. Thus not every newly discovered letter is reproduced (though all are listed). Similarly, the important manuscripts relating to the Kendal Friends School have been quoted from, not printed in extenso. Though they certainly deserve fuller publication, that would upset the balance of the present work. I should also emphasize that I have deliberately excluded documents crucial to an understanding of Dalton's scientific development, but already long-published and widely available, through frequent quotation and reproduction in standard secondary sources.

The following chapters also treat central aspects of Dalton's social situation and intellectual achievement in greater depth than others have attempted. I have endeavored to understand him not in terms of heroic biography but as a man through whose life we may explore the changing nature of British science at a crucial juncture in its social history. I have also tried to display some of the broader historical and historiographical problems attending both the specific analysis of natural knowledge in the Industrial Revolution, and the wider attempt to capture and subdue the past—that strange amalgam of significant, documented events, their shifting and enriching record, and the present light on which we necessarily depend.

The two immediately following chapters both have this broader cast. In chapter 2, I endeavor to outline the social context against which John Dalton's life and work must be understood. I also highlight some of the graver misrepresentations in the received picture of Dalton and explore the present state of our understanding. In chapter 3, I concentrate on an important and neglected key to an adequate historical appreciation of Dalton's intellectual achievement, that is, on the historiography of his development of the chemical atomic theory. With this broader background provided, subsequent chapters deal with narrower, more traditionally focused questions. Readers unfamiliar with previous Dalton scholarship may in fact prefer to begin with chapter 4, which discusses his life, and chapter 5, which investigates the formation of the chemical atomic theory. In chapter 6, I provide new documents dealing with atomic theory and in chapter 7, a series of letters covering the whole of Dalton's adult life. A concluding bibliographic essay surveys the publications of the last century and a quarter, assessing their reliability and present uses within the changing and maturing field of Dalton scholarship.

Here it is only necessary to re-emphasize that the following pages offer new documents and critical essays, not a definitive account. Though often written about, John Dalton has rarely enjoyed that exact enquiry and analytical attention which first-rank figures demand and deserve. To what extent I have succeeded in these respects is for the reader to judge. I hope these present explorations will at least encourage students of the period to approach the statements of Victorian "authorities" with a healthy skepticism and to find for themselves how much of the unknown past of British science can still be reconstructed from that country's multivarious public and private archives, museums, and libraries.

2. John Dalton and the Wider Context

What Manchester thinks today,
London thinks tomorrow
Traditional

SCIENCE AND THE INDUSTRIAL REVOLUTION

The reciprocal relationships between science and the British Industrial Revolution are involved, indirect and important. They are also curiously unexplored. It is still often assumed that all significant questions have been exhausted, when science and technology are shown either to have been directly linked, or quite unconnected, at this time. The latter assumption has been more frequent. It began as a late-Victorian belief that before the mid-nineteenth-century science was too *primitive* to have had serious technological applications. The patterns of explanation set forth in Arnold Toynbee's classic *Lectures on the Industrial Revolution in England* (1884) show remarkable perdurability. Toynbee, certain of the irrelevance of science, found its very mention unnecessary. Reflecting the tradition he established, such a recent work as Phyllis Deane's *The First Industrial Revolution* (1965) fails to accord science even the dignity of an entry in the index, let alone a discussion in the text, so peripheral is its nature and development to the course of that revolution she wishes to describe.

Belief in the irrelevance of science similarly affects much of the discussion in the *Industrial Revolution* volume of the encyclopedic Oxford *History of Technology*. Aware of the seeming paradox of this position, E. J. Holmyard applied a more apologetic version of Toynbee's view to the narrower case of one crucial science. He argued that "until the close of the seventeenth century chemistry had not outgrown alchemical ideas . . . Such a background . . . had it persisted, would have effectively prevented the astonishing development of chemical industry so characteristic of the nineteenth century and later." [1] Earlier science was thus not merely primitive but wrong. Only when "correct" chemical theories were available could technology benefit from science. Suppressing for a moment surprise that such "wrong" and alchemical ideas as transmutation have apparently not prevented the growth of the nuclear power industry, we should rather focus on the historiographical question.

As so often in historical writing, a peculiar complex of assumptions, born out of particular triumphs, anxieties, and problems in the contemporary society, linger on long after their utility has vanished. Earlier science quite naturally seemed irrelevant to eminent Victorians, flushed with pride in the startling triumphs of the later nineteenth century. Today our perspectives are rather different. Yet to clear away the tangled undergrowth of a century-long tradition will not be simple.

Any systematic investigation of such a subtle, rich, and complex theme as science in the Industrial Revolution will have to include a great range of elements. Four are immediately obvious.

1) The first is an appreciation of the actual scientific basis of Industrial Revolution technique (as example, how today the alternative series of reactions involved when cloth is bleached by sour milk, dilute sulphuric acid, and chlorine would be explained). Without a clear understanding of which of the period's techniques are scientifically obscure even today and which are now fully and predictively explicable, discussion of the relationship between *theoria* and *praxis* is bound to end in confusion and misunderstanding. Yet even this sort of information, although necessary, is not sufficient. Knowledge of the presently accepted theo-

1. C. Singer et al., eds., *A History of Technology* (Oxford, Clarendon Press, 1954–1958), IV, 214.

retical explanation of a technical process should not obscure an additional and historically more important question.

2) The second element in any adequate discussion is the question of the *apparent scientific basis* at the time. The fact that bleaching was given a phlogistic explanation does *not* mean (Holmyard to the contrary, notwithstanding) that no useful predictive science underlay contemporary bleaching practice. Indeed one of the most obvious, striking, and unexplored aspects of the Industrial Revolution is the ideologically based conviction many of its leaders shared, that their triumphs were indeed due to the advance and correct application of science. Hindsight may now indicate otherwise. But that they believed it so is a matter of very considerable psychological and practical importance.[2]

3) The third element in any enquiry is the effect of technological pressures on the course of scientific investigation and, conversely, the impact of theoretical advances on the pattern of industrial development. It has recently been fashionable to ignore the former question, while the latter has traditionally been considered applicable only to the period after 1850. Both the fashion and the tradition are unfortunate. The discussion of the interaction of theory and practice has also been bedevilled by overly simplistic Marxist assertions, and their equally simpleminded denial. Boris Hessen may have been misguided to stress so heavily that "in order to develop its industry, the bourgeoisie needed science," and thus to make "the development and flourishing of the bourgeoisie" the essential motor of progress. Alexander Koyré was equally misleading in his counterstatement that "science, the science of our epoch, like that of the Greeks, is essentially *theoria,* a search for the truth . . . an inherent and autonomous development." Such rhetorical antitheses are best forgotten. Unhappily their polarizing influence is still powerful.[3] The state of the histo-

2. See the remarks in C. C. Gillispie, "The Natural History of Industry," *Isis 48* (1957), 398–407. This pioneering exploration draws attention to one neglected aspect in its insistence that "the eighteenth-century application of science to industry was little more and nothing less than the attempt to develop a natural history of industry."

3. For the quoted statements and a fuller discussion of the historiography of science, see A. Thackray, "Science: Has Its Present Past a Future?" in R. Steuwer, ed.,

riographic art is thus such that one needs to stress continually how the reciprocal relations of science and technology can be both *real* and *indirect* because mediated by social institutions and assumptions which themselves vary widely, depending upon the science, the technology, the country, and the period. Happily the relationship between industrial expansion and the social organization of science is more immediate and easier to handle.

4) The effect of industrial, commercial, and economic growth upon the forms and institutions of science is the fourth element that invites attention. The first Industrial Revolution transformed Britain's manufactures, expanded her economy beyond recognition, and between 1760 and 1840 more than doubled her population. That science, like everything else, did not emerge unchanged, is scarcely surprising. Dramatic alterations in the employment opportunities for men of science—especially in popular, liberal arts and medical education—were one early result. Industrial entrepreneurship, agricultural improvement, government advising, periodical publishing, textbook writing, and ministering to the newly swollen scientific estate were other fields in which the enterprising found fresh outlets. Specialization within science and the formation of new scientific institutions were two inevitable by-products. A third was the slow but remorseless change in the class basis and social prestige of the scientific enterprise, as natural knowledge and private understanding gave way to trained and organized common sense and public debate about national priorities. The relationship of natural knowledge to ideology, and the importance attributed to science by contending social groups within an urbanizing and industrializing culture, are crucial but as yet unexamined keys to any full explication of the social transformations in British science at this time.

The enumeration of these four elements is sufficient to suggest some of the complexities and challenges. Attaining an adequate grasp of the interrelations of science and industrial change is a matter of no small concern in a world now dominated by the sci-

Historical and Philosophical Perspectives of Science, Minnesota Studies in the Philosophy of Science, no. 5 (Minneapolis, University of Minnesota Press, 1970), 112–127.

ence-technology relationship and its powers for good and ill. The subject is thus a natural one for new and significant research activity. More immediately, it is only with a sensitive awareness of this complex and shifting background, that any adequate appraisal can be made of John Dalton's life, scientific work, and changing place in history. Conversely, attention to these more limited and local questions may offer insights and information that bear on the larger issues.

THE PROFESSIONALIZATION OF SCIENCE

The period of the first Industrial Revolution—and of John Dalton's life—was the period in which British science was undergoing that series of transformations normally grouped under the label of professionalization. In the case of science, professionalization is a shorthand term for an unusually complex set of changes. Central to these changes is the gradual shift from natural knowledge seen as areas of enquiry subsidiary to other social pursuits (medicine, for example) and other intellectual concerns (such as theology) to that same knowledge seen as a collection of independent mental disciplines, each with its own particular tools, techniques, traditions, and central problems. Allied to this cognitive reordering is a social one. Professionalization in its broad sense includes, indeed revolves around, the change from practitioners whose livelihood is quite independent of, and may well be remote from, the new intellectual discipline, to practitioners who gain their sustenance from positions (whether teaching, research, technical, or administrative) allied to the discipline itself.[4] A third element in professionalization takes its rise from this second shift. It is the change to a world in which rewards (whether in esteem or whether translated into prizes or jobs) are primarily based on intellectual performance within the discipline,

4. It is useful to distinguish between the creation of a *cognitive* and a *professional* identity for any new discipline. Both are necessary if a field of learning is to be fully institutionalized. For further references and discussion see A. Thackray and R. K. Merton, "On Discipline Building: the Paradoxes of George Sarton," *Isis* (Winter 1972).

according to its own standards. This last alteration, in rewards, is allied to a fourth and final change—the shift to a structure in which societies, laboratories, journals, and teaching systems are organized around advancement of the discipline and its adherents.

These latter aspects of professionalization—the creation of jobs, reward structures and discipline-promoting systems—grow out of a new intellectual and social self-awareness among adherents of the discipline, and inevitably lead into the politics of legitimation and justification. In a world of scarce resources, a profession can only grow to the extent that it is successful in capturing social support among strategic interest groups. It is this harsh necessity that lies behind the intellectual and utilitarian claims so often stridently advanced as an individual science, or a group of disciplines, reaches the point at which wider social support is a prerequisite to further growth and change. In the particular case of the natural sciences in Industrial Revolution Britain, contemporary social philosophies of laisser-faire, self-help, and individualism made the need for effective propaganda and myth-making all the more urgent.

The social shifts just discussed may also be viewed in a slightly different way, one that is more helpful in understanding science in Industrial Revolution Britain. The emergence of distinct intellectual disciplines may still be regarded as the first stage, both chronologically and analytically. In the second, a critical mass of "men of science" emerges, possessing a sense of professional identity and loyalty to the scientific enterprise. Yet because of the weak and diffuse social structures of the different disciplines and their lack of individual critical mass in Britain, practitioners within a given discipline feel a greater identification with the overall scientific enterprise than with their own particular speciality. The "politics of justification" thus centers on science itself, rather than on any particular constituent discipline. The third stage is when cognitive and professional identity coincide, and both find their focus in university laboratories, research schools, and faculty positions.

It was the second of these three stages, that of the growing self-awareness of men of science, and of the increasing rhetorical and political action aimed at legitimating professional science rather than individual sciences, which coincided with and derived energy and support from the Industrial Revolution. Those same men who found a convenient public forum through the creation of the British Association for the Advancement of Science, saw in the ageing John Dalton a powerful symbol. Thus one set of myths was born. Forty years later, with professionalization entering its third stage, the university scientists of Owens College and its chemical research school were to recast Dalton as Manchester's first professional chemist.

THE SIGNIFICANCE OF MANCHESTER

It is against the twin backgrounds of the Industrial Revolution and of professionalization that Manchester science, as seen in its institutions, personnel, and leading ideas, assumes a particular importance.

Manchester was a prime focus of the first Industrial Revolution. Between 1760 and 1840 it passed from peaceful village to archetypal industrial city and herald of the new age. Its population multiplied tenfold. "What Manchester thinks today, London thinks tomorrow" was no idle boast. Contemporaries were acutely aware of the transformation, its supposed scientific basis, and its universal significance. Such percipient and opposing observers as Benjamin Disraeli and Friedrich Engels were agreed in their assessment. Disraeli put the optimists' case in his assertion that "what Art was to the ancient world, Science is to the modern; the distinctive faculty. In the minds of men the useful has succeeded to the beautiful . . . rightly understood, Manchester is as great a human exploit as Athens." The darker side was well caught in Engel's *Condition of the Working Class in England*. Yet even Engels could not help admitting that "modern times can show few greater marvels than the recent history of South Lancashire . . . [Bleaching] dyeing and calico printing [have all] benefitted from the rapid extension of chemical knowledge . . . [Manchester] is the masterpiece of the Industrial Revolution." [5]

The conviction of contemporaries as to the importance of Manchester and its science is well borne out by the roll call of famous names associated with the city in this period—from Thomas Percival and Thomas Henry, through John Dalton and William Henry to Eaton Hodgkinson, William Sturgeon, and James Prescott Joule. Such a list of names is indicative of the way that the values of professionalizing science were not merely compatible with, but in active mutual reinforcement to the values of the new manufacturing and commercial classes of the classic center of the Industrial Revolution. This reinforcement found its clearest expression in Manchester's oldest, most illustrious, and most intriguing scientific institution, its Literary and Philosophical Society. It was within and through the Society that John Dalton was to create his own particular contributions to the intellectual and social development of science.

DALTON IN CONTEXT

Dalton studies have been caught in a five-way trap. Its prongs consist of Dalton's own false modesty, the sloth of his first biographer, his symbolic value to the early and mid-Victorian professionalizers of science, his mythological function in the expanding chemistry department of Owens College, Manchester, and his identification with a form of chemical atomism the twentieth century has abandoned.

It is simplest to deal with the last point first. Perhaps the greatest achievement of historians of science over the last two decades has been their recapturing of the intellectual content and excite-

5. B. Disraeli, *Coningsby, or the New Generation* (1844. The quotation is from p. 148 of the 1948 [Lehmann] edition with introduction by W. Allen.); F. Engels, *The Condition of the Working Class in England* (original German edition, 1845. The quotation is from pp. 16–17 of the 1958 English edition [Oxford, Blackwell,] by W. O. Henderson and W. H. Chaloner). On Manchester see A. Briggs, *Victorian Cities* (1963); W. H. Thomson, *A History of Manchester to 1852* (Altrincham, 1967).

ment of "dead" science. It is thus no longer a bar to understanding that chemists today do not accept Dalton's theories. Instead, historians have restored his chemical atomism to its rightful context, where it may be appreciated for the great advance it was rather than dismissed as simply wrong.

The situation regarding studies of Dalton's life is far less satisfactory. The myths he so willingly fostered in his old age still obscure discussion. W. C. Henry is also much to blame. The reluctant, hurried, and uncritical biography he produced in 1854 relied heavily on anecdotes of Dalton's later years. Its broad outline was accepted by such later biographers as R. A. Smith (1856), Henry Lonsdale (1874), H. E. Roscoe (1895), and J. P. Millington (1905). The stereotype of Dalton as the brilliant autodidact, the scientist interested only in abstract truth and untouched by outside pressures, was embedded in the literature. No serious attempt at reappraisal was made until 1959.[6]

Consider, for instance, Dalton's own 1833 statement of how at age twelve he began "to teach the village school," was then "occasionally employed in husbandry for a year or more," and when fifteen moved to Kendal "as assistant in a boarding school." Like all Dalton's public utterances, the statement is scrupulously correct. Yet it hides more than it reveals. The picture conveyed is one of extremely limited opportunity, of a man triumphing over unpromising circumstance by sheer force of character. Henry willingly accepted and reinforced this and other aspects of the elderly Dalton's pose: witness the detailing of Dalton's "extreme reluctance to increase the small scientific library belonging to the Literary and Philosophical Society," or his reproving pupils for their "disposition to buy books" and claiming "that he could carry his library on his back, and yet had not read half of the books which constituted it." [7]

Now consider the available facts. Despite his own modest in-

6. The biographies are listed in A. L. Smyth's *John Dalton. A Bibliography of Works by and about Him* (Manchester, 1966) and discussed in F. Greenaway, "The Biographical Approach to John Dalton," *Manchester Memoirs 100* (1958–1959).

7. W. C. Henry, *Memoirs of the Life and Scientific Researches of John Dalton* (1854), pp. 2 and 236. On Henry, see ch. 3, n. 5, below.

come and the comparatively high price of books, it is not difficult to establish that Dalton owned 53 works in 1800, and over 700 at his death.[8] He was also borrowing books from, then acting as librarian for, the Literary and Philosophical Society within two years of election to membership.[9] Indeed on first arriving in Manchester, he quickly wrote to his former patron, Elihu Robinson, about the "3000 volumes" available in the New College where he lived, and about the superb resources of Chetham's, which Dalton correctly described as a "large library, furnished with the best books in every art, science, and language which is open to all, gratis."[10] That he should write to Robinson about books is only natural. It was in the latter's home that Dalton—at about the age of ten—had first made contact with an adequate library. And if even the small village of Eaglesfield, Cumberland, could offer such learning, how much more was available in Kendal. There the fifteen-year-old Dalton had access to the excellent philosophical library of his new patron and friend John Gough (who "has the advantage of all the books he has a mind for," his father having "furnished him with every necessary help").[11] The boarding school where Dalton taught was also vital to his own education. Following Henry's lead, every biography has damned this school with that faint praise the obscure provinces unthinkingly attract. Yet its newly purchased library included such mundane items as Robert Boyle's *Works*, Buffon's *Natural History*, John Flamsteed's *Historia Coelestis* and Newton's *Principia*. And no irony was intended when a contemporary circular soliciting *pupils* stressed this "choice collection of books in the most serviceable branches of science purposely prepared for the benefit and utility of the school."[12] Clearly the legends about Dalton's limited reading need treating with some reserve.

8. See ch. 5, n. 9, below and *The Late Dr. Dalton's Effects* (Manchester Central Library, Tract H 93).

9. Greenaway, "Biographical Approach," pp. 19–21.

10. H. Lonsdale, *John Dalton*, The Worthies of Cumberland, no. 5 (1874), pp. 9–98. The riches of Chetham's Library at this period may be assessed from J. Radcliffe, *Bibliotheca Chethamensis*, 2 vols. (Manchester, 1791).

11. Henry, *Memoirs of Dalton*, p. 10.

12. See ch. 4 below, esp. n. 4.

The schooling of one whom Henry saw as "emphatically self-taught" also warrants a fresh look. First we might note that the Society of Friends took literacy, modern learning, and the education of its children with the utmost seriousness, as the above quotation indicates. Then we might add some characteristic testimony of the period about the schools of the remoter North. "It is observed at Cambridge" said Gilbert Wakefield, second wrangler in 1776, "and is generally true that the hard progeny of the North, from Cumberland, Westmoreland and the remote parts of Yorkshire, are usually the profoundest proficients in mathematics and philosophy. A previous foundation for the superstruction of academic pursuits is usually laid in the schools of the northern parts of the country." [13]

Finally, what of Dalton's own particular experience? He did indeed attend the village school until the age of twelve. That its master John Fletcher made a deep and favorable impression is apparent not only from Dalton's career, but from the touching letter he wrote Fletcher some thirty-odd years later (Chapter 7, letter 18). Dalton also quickly attracted the patronage, aid, and encouragement of Elihu Robinson, a distant cousin. Robinson in turn was not only a prominent local Quaker, man of parts, and highly competent naturalist but one of sufficient affluence and scientific reputation to breakfast quite naturally with Sir Joseph Banks when in London. On moving to Kendal, Dalton was rapidly taken in tow by another Quaker philosopher, John Gough. Gough was an extremely proficient botanist, meteorologist, and mathematician who later tutored a succession of Cambridge wranglers, including no less a worthy than William Whewell.[14] They

13. Quoted in D. A. Winstanley, *Unreformed Cambridge* (Cambridge, Cambridge University Press, 1935), p. 55. On the importance of Quaker and Northern schools, see N. Hans, *New Trends in Education in the Eighteenth Century* (1951), *passim;* S. Pollard, *The Genesis of Modern Management* (Arnold, 1965), ch. 4.

14. For details of Gough's life and work, see T. T. Wilkinson, "Biographical Notices of Some Liverpool Mathematicians," *Transactions of the Historical Society of Lancashire and Cheshire 14* (1862), 29–40; and see *Westmorland Gazette,* 7 June 1884. A few of his mss. survive in Kendal Public Library and the County Record Office, Carlisle. From the latter it appears that Gough was a close friend of William Withering, of Lunar Society fame.

came many miles to sit at his feet; Dalton had only to stroll down the street. And should he stay at home, in his lodging at the school, he could always browse in the library or experiment with what was virtually his own private £52 set of apparatus.

Dalton was of course exceptional in his persistence and intellectual ability. However, the study of his background and education has a more general interest. Like a radioactive tracer, his progress through the late-eighteenth-century's informal Quaker network of scientific contacts does much to highlight and explain one of the mechanisms by which increasing numbers of men of obscure birth were recruited to a life of science as the Industrial Revolution opened up a new range of teaching and entrepreneurial opportunities. For instance, Elihu Robinson, Dalton's early patron, kept up a vigorous correspondence with such figures as Richard Reynolds, the manufacturer, and Thomas Collinson, the banker.[15] The Kendal Friends School was rebuilt in 1773 with the aid of gifts from Reynolds and Abraham Darby of Coalbrookdale, the East Anglian banker John Gurney, and the London physician John Fothergill. How well integrated into a national and international community the Kendal Friends were may also be seen in the notices they received of vacancies for masters in Quaker schools; these include New York (1782), Ipswich (1799), London (1802), and Ackworth (1804). There was even an 1803 letter from London seriously requesting "a clever north country genius."[16]

Much fresh information on other matters besides Dalton's edu-

15. Robinson's interests and importance are revealed in 33 letters from Thomas Collinson, running from 1759 to 1806, now preserved in the Library of the Society of Friends, London. The very first letter deals with a microscope Collinson is sending, while later ones often discuss scientific books and events. Robinson's diaries, and 44 letters to him from Richard Reynolds the Quaker manufacturer, are in the same library. Carlisle Public Library possesses two volumes of correspondence between Robinson and Thomas Wilkinson, another Lake District Quaker. Typical of this latter correspondence is Robinson's November 1789 Query "What is doing in the literary world? What hope of improvement in religion, morals and humanity? How goes the slave trade? Does thy intellectual eye see as far as London?" (Jackson Collection, Ms. 1 F Wil, *1*, p. 100.) For general background see A. Raistrick, *Quakers in Science and Industry* (1950).

16. Ms. packet 70, Strong Room, Kendal Meeting House.

cation still awaits assessment. This despite the fact that there are
now six book-length lives, written over a period of more than a
century, besides the never-ending flow of shorter accounts.[17] The
surviving family papers tell much about the actual material
wealth of a modest Quaker clan.[18] The records of local meetings
of the Society of Friends reveal a great deal about births, marriages, movements, "disownings," and schooling in the Lake District at that time.[19] Indeed, the "obscurity" of Dalton's early activities says more about the sloth of Victorian enquirers than the
available facts. For instance, his progress in, and the difficulties
of, the local school may be followed with some exactness. In September 1780, it was recorded that "as Friends have no school master teaching at Pardshaw Hall at present, this Meeting orders
John Wilson to divide three pounds now in his hand (as part of
the interest received from the school stock) equally between two
school masters teaching at Eaglesfield and Greysouthen, John Dalton and John Wilson." A note of the following July records "5/3
given to John Dalton who has now given up school for the
present." [20] These two statements document and authenticate one
important Dalton myth, while illustrating the deep Quaker com-
mitment to education, so fruitful for the science of the period.

   The activities and importance of itinerant lecturers in natural
philosophy wait to be assessed from contemporary newspapers
and accounts. Consider the case of John Banks. Late in 1782 he
began a full twelve months of paid philosophical activity in Cum-

17. Notable among these, especially for its stress on Dalton's early years, is Sir
Harold Hartley's analysis in *Proceedings of the Royal Society of London*, series A,
300 (1967), 291–315.
   18. See Dalton (Eaglesfield) Mss., County Record Office, Carlisle, Ref. D/Da.
   19. For instance, the oft-repeated but unsubstantiated story of the "fecklessness"
of Joseph Dalton, John's father, would appear correct. He was disowned by the
Pardshaw Hall Meeting in November 1772 "for irregularities and misconduct and
not paying duly his just debts" (Pardshaw Hall Monthly Meeting Book, pp. 30–32.
In County Record Office, Carlisle, Ref. DFC/F/1, Item 87).
   20. Minutes of Pardshaw Hall Preparative Meeting, 1756–1801, pp. 109, 113. In
County Record Office, Carlisle, Ref. DFC/F/1, Item 68. It would also seem that,
contrary to what every subsequent biographer has asserted following W. C. Henry's
lead, John Dalton went to the Kendal school in 1781 not to join but to *replace* his
brother. Jonathan taught at Ackworth and Tamworth until 1785. (Removal Certifi-
cates, pp. 103, 141. Ms. packet 106, Strong Room, Kendal Meeting House.)

berland, lecturing in Kendal, Penrith, Whitehaven, Workington, Cockermouth, and Keswick. At this same period at least three other lecturers (Mr Weavor, with an "eiduranion or transparent orrery," Mr Atkinson, and Mr Walker, Junior) were also active in the area. The implications for the general scientific knowledge and sophistication of the local culture are apparent. These implications are reinforced by even the most casual examination of the *Cumberland Pacquet and Ware's Whitehaven Advertiser*. In the 1780's, it carried regular advertisements for scientific publications, news of William Herschel's telescopic discoveries and the French Academy's report on air balloons, occasional meteorological items (latterly from Dalton and Gough), and extensive information on philosophical lectures.[21]

If there is still much to learn about Dalton's life, his symbolic value to early and mid-Victorian Britain is highly instructive. Already by the 1780's natural knowledge was beginning to take on new focus and demand new contexts, as the creation of the Manchester Literary and Philosophical Society itself reveals. However, formal institutional change was severely inhibited by the thirty-year sequence that led from the French Revolution through the Peninsular and Napoleonic Wars, to economic depression and Peterloo. Natural philosophy itself was particularly vulnerable to attack through its easy equation with the godless materialism of the French *philosophes*. Only from the mid-1820's was modest and necessary reform within the larger body politic again clearly distinguishable from the threat of radical subversion. And not until this wider change had occurred could the reform of science itself be safely broached.

The growing ferment that erupted in such things as controversy over the Board of Longitude, bitter debate over the

21. See, e.g., *Cumberland Pacquet*, 5 November and 17 December 1782; 18 March, 29 April, 20 May, 10 and 24 June, 15 and 22 July, 16 September and 14 October 1783 (John Banks): 12 November and 10 December 1782 (Mr. Weavor): 30 March and 5 April 1784 (Mr. Walker, Jr.): 29 August 1787 (I. Atkinson): 2 January 1781 (Chambers's *Cyclopedia* and the *Encyclopedia Britannica*): 18 May 1784 (Air balloons): 10 January 1787 and 2 January 1788 (Gough and Dalton). For information on John Banks, see Hans, *New Trends*, p. 149.

appropriate character to be sought in leaders of the Royal Society, and the deliberate formation of a British Association for the Advancement of Science, is indicative of the powerful forces at work. The very period which saw this new vitality was also a time of dramatic loss for *English* science. Its intellectual giants and natural leaders were suddenly cut down. England's three Foreign Associates of the French *Académie* (Humphry Davy, William Hyde Wollaston, and Thomas Young) all died within a six-month period in 1828–29. This fact alone explains much of the emotional pressure behind the response to Charles Babbage's *Reflections on the Decline of Science in England* in the following year. Of the first-rank figures of the elder generation, only Dalton was left. He was seized on and lionized in the 1830's, as the newly emerging group of professional scientists sought to create its own norms and myths (see Figure 1).

Dalton was in fact an ideal symbol: the equable, talented, humble man of science, devoted to plain dealing and his own researches. An 1832 letter from Joseph John Gurney to his wife reveals how Quakers already viewed their illustrious companion. "I had . . . a memorable setting yesterday with John Dalton the great philosopher. I suppose he now stands at the top of the tree in chemistry and mathematics. Hast thou ever seen him? He is certainly like Sir Isaac Newton both in countenance, and I *think* in disposition—peculiarly modest and retiring. I had the feeling of his being a religious character—one who thro' many deep enquiries into created things, has not forgotten his Creator." [22] The broader scientific community was also quick to realize his possibilities—witness Adam Sedgwick instructing the 1833 meeting of the British Association that "from the hour he [Dalton] came from his mother's womb, the God of Nature had laid his hand upon his head, and he ordained him for the ministration of high philosophy." Thus called, and without any powerful apparatus or extensive personal means, Dalton had yet made "a name not perhaps equalled by that of any other living philosopher of the world." When William IV, sensitive to the new currents of

22. Library of the Society of Friends, London. Gurney Mss. 4, p. 130.

1. Dalton Representing British Science. From a lithograph of John Dalton (on the right) thanking Gerrit Moll, a Dutch professor, for his defense of British science against Babbage's attack: circulated at the 1834 Edinburgh meeting of the B.A.A.S. (Courtesy of Carlisle Public Libraries.)

the period and "wishing to manifest his attachment to science," granted a royal pension, the recipient was naturally John Dalton with his "beautiful moral simplicity and singleness of heart." Other tokens of social acceptance crowded in: honorary degrees from Oxford (1832) and Edinburgh (1834), presentation at Court (1834), a subscription fund of £2000 in Manchester to commission a statue by Chantrey (1833–34), the doubling of the pension itself (1836), appointment as Fellow and member of the Senate of the new London University (1836). In all these ways the world of the 1830's paid homage to the new idea of the professional scientist by honoring the last survivor from the period of prototypes.[23]

The recognition the *scientist* enjoyed in the "Age of Reform" was a far cry from that of Dalton's youth. His successful career in science was in fact made when the very idea of such a thing barely existed. Only by determined self-help could the elements be welded together: the modest teaching positions, the use of others' apparatus and laboratories, the fees for technological and utilitarian services, the reliance on public lectures to supplement a precarious basic income.[24] Despite his obvious abilities and predilections, it did not occur to the youthful Dalton or his older advisers that such a career was either possible or desirable. Yet it seems that by the 1780's and 90's science was beginning to recruit a new class of practitioners, men who found in the scientific enterprise not only their intellectual goals but their daily bread.

The emergence of this new class raised many problems, not least in the hostilities it introduced to the scientific enterprise.

23. W. C. Henry, *Memoirs of Dalton*, pp. 173–179. The decision on the pension was of course actually made by Lord Grey's ministry. A further illustration of Dalton's social prestige by this time is found on the title page of the 1834 second edition of his *Meteorological Observations and Essays* which lists him, inter alia, as "Honorary Member of the Royal Medical Society, Edinburgh: Of the Philosophical Societies of Bristol, Cambridge, Leeds, Sheffield and Yorkshire."

24. In this respect Humphry Davy's career makes an illuminating complement to Dalton's. Consider, for example, the way Davy was able to make of the Royal Institution his own research institute, or how in 1802 he had already located a virtual sinecure position that was to bring him over £1000 in Government money within a decade. This latter coup illustrates the advantages inherent in a Metropolitan situation. See J. A. Paris, *Life of Sir Humphry Davy* (1831), I, 372–373. See also ch. 4 below.

The "new men" of science with their provincial, Dissenting and lowlier values did not sit easily beside the Anglican and amateur natural philosophers of a more dilettante if more gracious tradition. Dalton's experience is instructive. It was after all not to London but to Edinburgh, that bastion of middle-class professionalism, that he journeyed in 1807 to make the first full and formal exposition of the chemical atomic theory. Just three years later he firmly declined to be put up for membership in the Royal Society of London. Election as corresponding member of the French *Académie* was a different matter, for that was an unambiguously professional honor. The contrast is still sharper. Though he journeyed to Paris in 1822 to take his seat and meet his peers, he apparently could not find time for similar formal ceremonies as a Fellow of the Royal Society till 1834, when even metropolitan English society was finally acknowledging professional science. This failure to respond to London's science was in no way owing to a churlish or withdrawn tendency on Dalton's part—witness his extremely active role in the Manchester Literary and Philosophical Society over half a century and his intimate (and little examined) involvement in the early affairs of the British Association for the Advancement of Science. The division was rather one of class and style, nicely illustrated when the first meeting of the British Association "then and there resolved that we were ever to be *Provincials*. Old Dalton insisted on this." [25]

Such displays of sturdy independence were curtailed by Dalton's strokes in 1837 and underplayed by eulogists and obituarists anxious to promote unity and professional science and to make Dalton their symbol. Later Victorians altered matters still further. Under the tutelage of the professional chemists of Owens College, Dalton slowly became a pure chemist—a transformation that his onetime pupil W. C. Henry had already considerably aided in his 1854 biography. Not only the physics of gases but also any active concern with technology, were slowly erased. One may search the work of Roscoe, A. N. Meldrum or J. R. Partington in vain for

25. A. Geikie, *The Life of Sir Roderick I. Murchison* (1875), I, 188. See also ch. 4 below.

adequate discussion of Dalton's interests in steam engines, dye-stuffs, bleaching, gas lighting, water analysis, or technical pharmacy. The Manchester school of chemists took the final step in removing the man from his context. They thus reinforced the late-Victorian myth of a sharp separation between pure science and practical technology in the Industrial Revolution. The list of Dalton's concerns just given suggests how inadequate is the picture they created.

Dalton's natural interest in immediate and local questions of practical importance seems to have been the key to his theoretical advances more than once. Technological problems undoubtedly served to focus his thought and enquiry. At the same time, it is apparent that the resulting progress in natural philosophy had no direct practical value to manufacturers faced by those problems which sparked Dalton's curiosity. Two examples will suffice. One stimulus to Dalton's abstract work on the physics of gases was displayed in the initial title of the April 1800 paper reporting that work: "Experimental essays, to determine the expansion of gases by heat, and the maximum of steam or aqueous vapour, which any gas of a given temperature can admit of: with observations on the common and improved steam engines." [26] The paper and its theory gave no immediate relief to the steam engine owner or manufacturer. Again, it is apparent that some of the crucial investigations that led to the chemical atomic theory (those on gas-water solubility and on the composition of gaseous hydrocarbons) were nourished in part by Dalton's familiarity with the new industry of gas-lighting and by his collaborator William Henry's active interest in the commercial production of aerated water. Yet the conscious application of chemical atomic theory was something in which neither gasworks manager nor soda water manufacturer indulged for many decades to come.

Where the natural philosopher was of immediate use to the practical man was in devising better methods of quality control, based on a judicious blend of theoretical knowledge and common

26. See the list of papers Dalton read to the Manchester Literary and Philosophical Society, as reproduced in Lonsdale, *Dalton*, pp. 309–318.

sense. Dalton acted in this way as consultant to Manchester's gas-works (he was also to testify before Parliamentary committees on gas making).[27] A rather different example may be found in his 1823 paper "On the nature and properties of indigo; with directions for the valuation of different samples." In this latter case the reaction of a Manchester cottonbroker who heard the paper is available. Absalom Watkin found the theoretical part rather poor, but thought important "one fact . . . the best indigo of commerce does not contain more than 45 per cent of pure indigo." [28] One final example of this consultant service is Dalton's considerable effort (papers in 1814 and 1819) over the chemical analysis of different waters, a matter of concern to the physician, the dyer, and the steam engine owner.

If technological problems could act to focus pure research, and if the man of science could offer some worthwhile consultant service to the manufacturer in the Industrial Revolution, there were additional ways in which abstract science and practical concerns could interact. One was in the ability of the natural philosopher to offer psychological support to the manufacturer, through the demonstration that practical operations not fully understood were yet susceptible to rational examination. No manufacturer could gain practical advantage from Dalton's "Observations on certain liquids obtained from caoutchouc by distillation," his papers "On muriatic acid" and "On the oxymuriate of lime," or his work on "Oil, and the gases obtained from it by heat." [29] Even his analyses of mine "damps" and his research on explosive mixtures [30] were of intellectual rather than practical value. However it was not unimportant to the developing economy of science that the enlightened industrialist found psychological reward in supporting such endeavors, while the new men of science found additional social legitimation through their pursuit.

This list of Dalton's technology-prompted investigations does

27. See ch. 7, n. 27.
28. A. E. Watkin, ed., *Absalom Watkin. Extracts from His Journal. 1814–1856* (Unwin, 1920), p. 97.
29. For details, see Lonsdale, *Dalton*, pp. 309–318.
30. See for example ch. 7, letter 26.

not accord well with the stereotype that his "mental tendencies were exclusively to meditation and abstract reasoning." [31] The movement toward redress is now slowly getting under way. Recent studies have shown a healthy and increasing awareness of Dalton's industrial and social context. The articles by A. Clow and D. S. L. Cardwell in the bicentenary volume on *John Dalton and the Progress of Science* (1968) illustrate the point, while the recent biographies by Greenaway and Patterson sketch some of the possibilities. The most sustained attempt at reappraisal is, however, indirect. It is to be found in the wealth of detailed information on the Manchester area now available in A. E. Musson's and E. Robinson's *Science and Technology in the Industrial Revolution* (1969). Their work spells out much that has long been implicit in Dalton's own life-story: the importance of provincial libraries, Dissenting and mathematical academies, itinerant lecturers, local scientific societies and institutions, and scientific knowledge and enthusiasm among early manufacturing entrepreneurs. The plethora of factual detail that they provide makes it apparent that Dalton was no isolated phenomenon, but simply the most scientifically talented representative of a whole social group. Musson's and Robinson's work provides a fascinating and invaluable natural history of this group and its scientific and technological activities.

Despite such welcome advances, Dalton studies are not yet entirely free from the five-pronged trap described earlier. The light of patient investigation has still to dispel many of the inherited myths. However, fruitful lines of investigation are now clear, and the overall content of Dalton's life is beginning to be better understood. This book aims to contribute to that growing understanding, by studying particular issues in depth. Such special studies, whether of John Dalton or other individuals, will also help bring into focus the deeper challenge: an adequate analytical and interpretive account not just of one man or one region, but of science in the British Industrial Revolution.

31. Henry, *Memoirs of Dalton*, p. 235.

3. Chemical Atomic Theory in History and Historiography

*Before John Dalton's discovery
of the laws of chemical combination, and without his atomic
theory to explain those laws,
chemistry as an exact science
did not exist . . . Dalton may
truly be said to be the founder
of modern chemistry.*

H. E. Roscoe in 1895

The reconstruction of the sequence by which Dalton was led to formulate his chemical atomic theory has, for more than a century now, provided one of the most tantalizing problems in the history of scientific thought. At a time when chemistry occupied the best minds of the day, in a way rarely paralleled before or since, it was the work of this provincial and stubbornly self-reliant *savant* that gave the science what has ever since remained its fundamental model of reality. Not unnaturally Dalton and the nature of his achievement were soon the subjects of a lively historical controversy. The rival claim of Bryan and William Higgins, actively supported by Humphry Davy and just as actively opposed by Thomas Thomson, provides the most obvious early instance of this controversy.[1] Allied to this minor but still continuing skirmish over questions of priority are two fascinating and far more fundamental problems.

One, just mentioned above, is the recovery of the actual history of Dalton's work. The other is closely related and equally demanding. It is to elucidate the historiography of Dalton's achievement. Although historians may not always advance an under-

1. The Higgins-Dalton priority dispute is exhaustively discussed in T. S. Wheeler and J. R. Partington, *The Life and Work of William Higgins* (Pergamon, 1960), pt. III. The historiographical account that follows is inevitably less than complete. It may be amplified by judicious use of the bibliographical information in J. R. Partington, *A History of Chemistry*, III (1962), chs. 15–17.

standing of their professed objects of study, their work cannot but cast light upon the values, attitudes, and assumptions of their own time. The changing historiography of chemical atomic theory thus offers insights into the changing utility and prestige of the theory itself. It also offers important clues to the unravelling of Dalton's own work, and reflects significant shifts in popular philosophies of science and history. Such an apparently esoteric subject may thus repay attention.

In fact the key to the long and confused history of attempts to explain the origins of Dalton's theory lies in three observations: that Dalton was not primarily, and certainly not initially, a chemist; that the history of science was till very recently the exclusive pursuit of often devoted, but perforce limited, amateurs; and that in the latter part of the nineteenth century Manchester became the home of a flourishing and influential school of chemistry.

THE EARLY ACCOUNTS

The earliest attempt to provide a historical explanation of Dalton's work was made by Thomas Thomson, Regius Professor of Chemistry at Glasgow, tireless scientific journalist and propagandist, friend of Dalton and supporter of his work, and writer of the first British text devoted solely to the history of chemistry. In keeping with the inductivist fashion of his times, Thomson was quite convinced that Dalton's theory had arisen out of chemically observed facts. In 1831 he informed the readers of his *History* how

[in 1803] Mr Dalton informed me that the atomic theory first occurred to him during his investigations of olefiant gas and carburetted hydrogen gases, at that time imperfectly understood, and the constitution of which was first fully developed by Mr Dalton himself . . . He found that if we reckon the carbon in each the same, then carburetted hydrogen gas contains exactly twice as much hydrogen as olefiant gas does. This determined him to state the ratios of these constituents in numbers, and to consider the olefiant gas as a compound of one atom of carbon and one atom of hydrogen; and carburetted hydrogen of one

atom of carbon and two atoms of hydrogen. The idea thus conceived was applied to carbonic oxide, water, ammonia, &c.; and numbers representing the atomic weights of oxygen, azote, &c., deduced from the best analytical experiments which chemistry then possessed.[2]

This account is delightfully clear. Unfortunately, it testifies more to Thomson's powers of imagination than to his concern for sober historical investigation.

Only six years before publishing the above account, Thomson had delivered himself of a considerably more cautious appraisal. In 1825, writing in a serious work of chemistry, not a popular history, he said: "I do not know when the ideas [of the atomic theory] first occurred to [Dalton]. In all probability they struck him by degrees, and were adopted in consequence of his own experimental investigations . . . Unless my recollection fails me, Mr Dalton's theory was originally deduced from his experiments on olefiant gas and carburetted hydrogen." Doubts as to Thomson's reliability as a witness are compounded by the fact that on a later occasion he attributed the origin of Dalton's theory to work on the nitrogen oxides.[3] Nonetheless the account in his 1831 *History* was unchallenged for a number of years. It fitted prevailing philosophical views, made eminent sense, and had the authentic tone of the eyewitness account. Reappraisal came only with the obituary notices that followed Dalton's death in 1844.

The most thoughtful obituary was provided by Dr. George Wilson. Unlike many writers on Dalton and his work, Wilson took the trouble to read Dalton's published papers. He saw at once how poorly Thomson's supposedly authoritative account fitted the available facts. After stating and dismissing Thomson's version, he went on to analyze the published papers, and from their sequence to demonstrate the steps by which Dalton was led

2. *The History of Chemistry* (1831), II, 291–292. Thomson's attempts to explain the origins of Dalton's atomic theory actually began with his involvement in the priority dispute with Higgins, in 1814. See *Annals of Philosophy* 3 (1814), 329–338.
3. *An Attempt to Establish the First Principles of Chemistry by Experiment* (1825), II, 9–11; *Proceedings of the Royal Philosophical Society of Glasgow* 3 (1850), 140.

to the chemical atomic theory. In his opinion " [Dalton] was test-
ing, by experiment, the truth of a hypothesis as to the cause of
the specific solubility of gases in water, which proved in the end
to be quite untenable; but, like Columbus, who missed an El
Dorado but found an America, he discovered something better."

Wilson's account was a notable feat of historical reconstruction. It was all the more remarkable in that it came from someone
who had " [no] access to any private sources of information" and
was relying solely on "works which are, or may be, in the hands of
all." [4] But although it showed admirable fidelity to the published
material and an excellent historical sense, Wilson's interpretation
had neither the logical simplicity and chemical orientation of
Thomson's version nor the esoteric power of an appeal to manuscript information not generally available. Wilson's conclusions
were soon forgotten. Only now, more than a century later, is his
thesis beginning to receive the recognition it deserves, thanks
largely to L. K. Nash's independent restatement of its message.

The man who did possess the Dalton manuscripts, and therefore the key to any fully satisfactory account, was W. C. Henry.
Henry was the only son of Dalton's contemporary, lifelong friend,
and (it would seem) intending biographer, William Henry. Unfortunately William predeceased his subject. The task therefore
devolved on W. C. Henry. And he is the real villain of the piece
so far as Dalton scholars are concerned. Promised Dalton's manuscripts as early as 1837, in order that he could write the definitive
biography, he prevaricated for over a decade. It was only a direct
invitation from the Cavendish Society in the spring of 1853 that
finally prompted him to action.[5]

4. *British Quarterly Review 1* (1845). The essay is reprinted in G. Wilson, *Reli-
gio Chemici* (1862); see pp. 332, 340. For Wilson, see the *DNB*.

5. See *Manchester Memoirs 57* (1912–1913), no. 19, p. 10; W. C. Henry, *Memoirs
of the Life and Scientific Researches of John Dalton* (1854), pp. vii–viii. From the
former reference it is apparent how weak was Henry's claim that on Dalton's death
he was surprised to learn of the bequest of manuscripts to him. In the published
Memoirs of Dalton he also had the temerity to blame the further long delay on
the "great reluctance" to part with Dalton's papers, manifested by Peter Clare, Dalton's closest friend and Henry's coexecutor. Yet though Clare died in 1851, Henry
had *still* not inspected the manuscripts when he received the Cavendish Society's

The biography was written within a year. It relied heavily on anecdotes supplied by a few friends, and made little use of the manuscripts that came to Henry from Dalton's *house*. No longer a Manchester resident, Henry made no effort to see what material might exist at the Literary and Philosophical Society itself. For more than forty years the "Lit and Phil" had been the home of Dalton's laboratory, the scene of his experimental investigations, the vehicle for most of his scientific communications, the auditorium for many of his public lectures, and the focus of his leisure hours. Henry's biography, boldly titled *Memoirs of the Life and Scientific Researches of John Dalton,* was written in blissful unawareness of the twelve volumes of laboratory notebooks, the more than 150 lecture diagrams, the many printed syllabuses, and the variegated manuscript notes which were to slumber on at the "Lit and Phil," undisturbed through a further four decades.

The lack of enthusiasm with which Henry approached his task is apparent from the careless and slipshod volume he finally produced. It is even more evident in a note he wrote to John Davy (reproduced in chapter 7 below). This complained about the "uneventful" nature of Dalton's life, the "quaintness and dryness in his style," and the "insensibility to literary elegance, which restrains his biographer within narrow limits." Nonetheless the biography was written. And even Henry could not resist discussing the origins of Dalton's theory.

Having first admitted that Wilson's obituary was "beyond comparison the ablest and justest appreciation that has yet appeared of Dalton's philosophical character and discoveries" Henry ignored its conclusions, preferring to rely on Thomas Thomson's account. To this he added further information from his own and his father's notes, suggesting that it was to J. B. Richter's earlier

request in the spring of 1853. Comments in their own later biographies of Dalton imply that both R. A. Smith and Henry Lonsdale began work when uncertain that Henry would ever deliver. The limitations of Henry's work are considered further in the Bibliographic Essay, below. His abandonment of the role of Manchester chemist for that of Herefordshire gentleman in 1837, and his reluctance to be reminded of his native town, are well displayed by K. and W. V. Farrar in a forthcoming work on the Henry family. I am indebted to them for the opportunity to read their study in manuscript.

work on chemical equivalents that Dalton owed his fundamental ideas. Henry was aware that all was not well. In fact he admitted that his added information "may even be thought to prove too much, and to be scarcely reconcilable with his [Dalton's] earlier communications to Dr Thomson, and with the view of the atomic doctrine I have endeavoured to maintain." Having said this, he prevaricated, suggesting that "Dalton had patiently and maturely reflected on all the phenomena of chemical combination known to him," admitting that Dalton's "fresh utterances to Dr Thomson . . . [were] more likely to be accurate," and lamely justifying his inclusion of Dalton's reported allusions to Richter's work on the grounds that "it is the obvious duty of a conscientious historian to record faithfully all documents in his possession." [6]

However inadequate, Henry's book became the standard Dalton biography, if only by default. The line it laid down was followed by such other biographers as R. A. Smith and Henry Lonsdale, and by chemical historians like C. A. Wurtz and E. S. C. von Meyer. Thomson's inductivist version of how Dalton arrived at his theory was thus slowly embedded in the literature, while Wilson's far more perceptive account was allowed to sink into oblivion. But at the very time that the historical myth was being firmly established, developments which would eventually undermine its whole foundation were taking place in Manchester.

THE "MANCHESTER SCHOOL" OF CHEMISTS

Thanks to the creation of Owens College, and the brilliant thirty-year reign of H. E. Roscoe, later Victorian Manchester became the center of Britain's first fully professional school of chemistry. Members of the school pressed history into service as one minor weapon in their quest for legitimation, prestige, and support. It is this circumstance which, more than any other, accounts for the new interest in Dalton apparent among members of the "Lit and Phil" toward the close of the nineteenth century.

Dalton's apparatus—bequeathed, like his manuscripts, to W. C.

6. Henry, *Memoirs of Dalton*, pp. x, 84–86.

Henry—actually never left the Society's premises. Manifesting the reluctance to be involved that has already been noted, Henry simply presented it to the Society. There the apparatus "remained enclosed in unsightly boxes, in a back room" until 1858. Then, thanks to money left over from a Watt monument fund, it was belatedly mounted and put on display.[7] The manuscripts did not fare so well. The biography finished, Henry gave his Dalton papers to the "Lit and Phil." In the annual report for 1862 they are euphemistically described as being "preserved in the archives of the Society," and for many years no more was heard of them. A change in attitude was finally brought about by the combined effect of a variety of late-nineteenth-century events. Among these were the creation of the Wilde bequest, the revolutionary work going on in physics, and more especially the historical enthusiasm of H. E. Roscoe.

Roscoe was the maternal great-grandson of the last rector of the ill-fated Warrington Academy and member of a distinguished family of Liverpool Dissenters. He was also one of Bunsen's most brilliant pupils at Heidelberg. Returning to England and private practice in 1856, he was soon applying for the post of chemistry professor in Manchester's newly established Owens College. When Roscoe joined the College in 1857 as successor to Edward Frankland, its fortunes were at their lowest ebb. Only 33 students remained. When, almost thirty years later, he resigned his chair, the College boasted 745 students and it was estimated that no fewer than 2,000 pupils had passed through the chemical laboratory.[8] Roscoe's role in Victorian science, educational reform, and public life awaits detailed investigation. Here the discussion must be confined to the brilliant school of chemistry he established, and more particularly to the strong historical inter-

---

7. *Proceedings of the Manchester Literary and Philosophical Society 1* (1860), 53.

8. On Sir Henry Enfield Roscoe (1833–1915), see T. E. Thorpe, *The Right Honourable Henry Enfield Roscoe. A Biographical Sketch* (Longmans, 1916). On Owens College, and esp. the success of its chemistry department, see P. J. Hartog, ed., *The Owens College, Manchester. A Brief History of the College and Description of its Various Departments* (Manchester, 1900); also H. E. Roscoe, *Record of Work Done in the Chemical Department of the Owens College, 1857–1887* (MacMillan, 1887).

ests its members displayed. When we appreciate that in the half-century before 1914 the Manchester department had among its staff and students, for shorter or longer periods, such well-known historians of chemistry as Roscoe, Arthur Harden, Carl Schorlemmer, T. E. Thorpe, M. M. Pattison Muir, P. J. Hartog, A. N. Meldrum, and J. R. Partington, we can better understand why Dalton was to prove so fascinating and attract so much attention.

The first sign of Roscoe's interest came in 1874, in the dedication and preface of Lonsdale's eminently readable biography.[9] Roscoe's curiosity was evidently aroused. Later that same year he was lecturing on the origin of Dalton's theory and addressing the "Lit and Phil" on Dalton's measurements of atomic weight. In 1876 he was giving the earliest serious description of Dalton's apparatus.[10] A year later the first volume of "Roscoe and Schorlemmer," a book destined to be the classic *Treatise on Chemistry* for more than a generation, appeared. Its frontispiece is a portrait of Dalton, its text is copious in historical detail, and its claim explicit that "Dalton's atomic theory may be said . . . to have exerted an influence on [chemistry's] progress greater than that of any other generalization, with, perhaps, the single exception of Lavoisier's explanation of the phenomena of combustion." [11] So far Roscoe's reports, although unambiguous in their enthusiasm for Manchester's great early chemist, were based solely on the secondary literature.

The crucial moment came when, in his role as eminent man of science and general editor of the Century Science Series, he set to work to write the introductory volume for that excellent set of biographies. *John Dalton and the Rise of Modern Chemistry* appeared in 1895. As the title makes clear, the Manchester school of professional chemists by now saw Dalton as their patron saint and

9. *John Dalton*, The Worthies of Cumberland, no. 5 (1874).

10. See *Science Lectures for the People*, 6th series (Manchester, 1875), pp. 15–27; *Proceedings of the Manchester Literary and Philosophical Society 14* (1875), 35–41; *15* (1876), 77–82.

11. H. E. Roscoe and C. Schorlemmer, *A Treatise on Chemistry*, 3 vols. (1877–1884). See vol. I, p. 65. The *Treatise* reached a fifth English edition as late as 1920.

were not afraid to interpret his life accordingly. To quote Roscoe, in one of his clearest displays of a pride at once provincial and Victorian: "Dalton may truly be said to be the founder of modern chemistry. As with the indestuctibility of matter, so with the indestructibility of energy. What Dalton did for the first great principle, Joule accomplished for the second: and he is therefore the founder of modern physics. And thus the great twin brethren of Manchester did work for the world the like of which hath not been seen, and the importance of which cannot be reckoned." [12] Roscoe fashioned his biography accordingly. As its contents make clear, he was by then aware that a considerable amount of unexploited Dalton manuscript was available at the "Lit and Phil."

Since the depression of 1873, the Society itself had been in a period of steady decline. Dropping attendance and an ageing membership were the symptoms of the malaise affecting this general scientific association in an increasingly discipline-oriented world. Partial relief came early in 1895, with a generous bequest from a wealthy manufacturing member. The "Wilde endowment" provided a variety of new facilities, chief among which was the salary for a full-time "Assistant Secretary and Librarian." An appointment to the post in July 1895 had an immediate and dramatic effect on the Society's library.[13] Whether the prospect of a new hand at work prompted Roscoe to publish what he had already discovered is not known, though possible. The limited hints and allusions which could be included in a popular biography were by themselves quite insufficient. His full-scale "New view of the genesis of Dalton's atomic theory, derived from original manuscripts" was offered to the British Association for the Advancement of Science at its annual meeting in September 1895. The paper, like the well-known book of similar title that followed it in the spring of 1896, was written in collaboration by Roscoe and his colleague Arthur Harden.[14]

12. *John Dalton and the Rise of Modern Chemistry* (1895), p. 10.
13. *Manchester Memoirs 40* (1896), 105–108.
14. For Sir Arthur Harden (1865–1940), see A. Findlay and W. H. Mills, eds., *British Chemists* (Chemical Society, 1947), pp. 270–286. A pupil of Roscoe's and eventual Nobel prize winner, Harden in the 1890's "lectured to the [Owens] hon-

That two University scientists should publish a volume of historical studies did not at that time occasion the surprise it would today. After all, no less a physicist than James Clerk Maxwell took it upon himself to edit the *Electrical Researches* of Henry Cavendish, while it was a committee of Cambridge scientists that drew up the now well-known 1888 *Catalogue of the Portsmouth Collection of Books and Papers Written by or Belonging to Sir Issac Newton.* Perhaps a long-established Mancunian desire to exhibit Dalton as the "Newton of chemistry" played an unconscious part in Roscoe and Harden's work. At all events the appearance of their "contribution to chemical history" was to signal the end of the Thomson myth.

As early as 1874 Roscoe had been stressing that *"the idea introduced by Dalton was the idea of weight."* Now, thanks to the discoveries at the "Lit and Phil," he could assert that Dalton "arrived at the idea that the atoms of different substances have different weights from purely physical considerations. This at once led him to conceive of chemical combination as taking place between varying numbers of atoms of definite weight, a position which he then succeeded in confirming by the results of analyses . . . It was the theory of the existence of atoms of different weights which led Dalton to the discovery of the facts of combination in multiple proportions." [15] So, simply and neatly, the myth of Dalton the inductivist chemist was exploded and that of Dalton the chemist with a strictly hypothetico-deductive approach deftly inserted in its place.

Of course there was a lot more to the *New View* than this, but this was its ruling vision. Accordingly, its authors chose to quote from Dalton's newly discovered laboratory notebooks just such passages as would support their interpretation and to ignore more awkward parts.[16] They reproduced in full Dalton's fascinating

---

our students on the history of chemistry, a subject in which he was greatly interested." See also *Reports of the British Association for the Advancement of Science* 65 (1895), 656, and H. E. Roscoe and A. Harden, *A New View of the Origin of Dalton's Atomic Theory* (1896).

15. See *Science Lectures*, p. 16, and Roscoe and Harden, *New View*, pp. viii–ix.

16. As they point out (p. 54), their summary contains only "a few quotations" from Dalton's notebooks. Naturally these support their interpretation of the devel-

1810 account of the origins of the chemical atomic theory. Yet they promptly dismissed his 1805 dating of some ideas because it conflicted with their view of the hypothetico-deductive chemist.[17] Like previous writers on Dalton they were dominated by the chemical *consequences* of his work and the corresponding vision of Dalton as above all a chemist. Though applying the favorite late-nineteenth-century historical technique of detailed examination of manuscript sources, Roscoe and Harden were no more able to escape from their own interpretative bias than those German historians they emulated. For all their marshalling of documents, these two leading members of the Manchester school of professional chemists could not avoid a narrow chemical approach.

The *New View* remains an impressive piece of work, and one invaluable now that Dalton's laboratory notebooks have perished. Even so it fed rather than finished the growing debate over Dalton's work. The 1890's were after all a period of rapidly increasing interest in the internal structure of matter. This interest culminated in J. J. Thomson's determination of e/m, the Curies' work on radium, and Ernest Rutherford and Frederick Soddy's observation of spontaneously occurring "transmutations." The final vindication of all those who had doubted the literal truth of the chemical atomic theory, together with the demonstration of new and unsuspected atomic properties, naturally caused a renewal of interest in the man who originated the theory—a renewal nicely aided by the 1903 centenary of Dalton's original table of atomic weights.[18]

One result of this new interest was a long series of papers by

opment of Dalton's thought. For example, their reference (p. 64) to page 107 of notebook ii gives no hint that pages 109 and 111 of that same notebook contain material difficult to reconcile with their 1803 dating of Dalton's "second theory of mixed gases." This additional material is reproduced in *Manchester Memoirs* 55 (1910–1911), no. 5, pp. 15–16.

17. Roscoe and Harden, *New View*, p. 25.

18. The new interest in Dalton among members of the "Lit and Phil" over the twenty years after 1895 must also be seen in the light of such events as Soddy's 1904 Wilde lecture to the Society, and the many papers presented by Rutherford and his collaborators, following Rutherford's 1907 assumption of the Manchester chair of physics.

A. N. Meldrum. Really a historian at heart, Meldrum had earlier obtained a D.Sc. with his thesis on *Avogadro and Dalton: the Standing in Chemistry of Their Hypotheses*. In Manchester as a Carnegie research fellow, his attention soon turned to the origins of the chemical atomic theory. Making the first sustained effort to place Dalton fully within his chemical context, Meldrum produced a series of studies of enduring value. Unfortunately he too was blinded by the vision of Dalton as above all a *chemist*. Meldrum was fully aware that the Thomson myth was exploded, but he was equally dissatisfied with Roscoe and Harden's account. He therefore sought to remodel the classical inductivist version, basing it on the slight foundation of the first reference to the nitrogen oxides, in Dalton's experimental notes for 4 August 1803. The inadequacies of Meldrum's attempt are now well known, yet his articles remain of great interest. They are particularly valuable for their occasional quotations from Dalton's notebooks, notebooks of which Meldrum unfortunately made little use, except for the express purpose of confuting Roscoe and Harden.[19]

Just how rich, and how incompletely exploited, was the Manchester Society's store of Dalton manuscripts is well illustrated by events in the summer of 1914. "Whilst preparing a catalogue of the apparatus and other property in the House of the Society," a special committee encountered "a roll of diagrams in one of the cupboards." Further search brought to light no less than 150 separate diagrams, prepared by Dalton in connection with a variety of public lectures. In order to sort and identify those diagrams it was necessary "to examine the Dalton manuscripts in the possession of the Society." "A number of lecture notes and syllabuses of courses of lectures were found" in the course of this examination. Their inspection led to the not altogether surprising conclusion that "the accounts published of the lectures of Dalton have been very incomplete" and that "few have realized the important posi-

---

19. Meldrum's papers may be found in the *Manchester Memoirs* for 1909–1911. For an appreciation of his historical work, see *Journal of the Chemical Society* (1934), pp. 1476–1478; for the weakness of his inductivist version, L. K. Nash, "The Origin of Dalton's Chemical Atomic Theory," *Isis* 47 (1956), 101–116.

tion that his lectures . . . had in his lifework." The intention was then stated "later to detail certain of these lectures more fully." Unhappily this intention was not fulfilled. However, there is in existence what amounts to a detailed catalog of the syllabuses and diagrams, though not of the lecture notes.[20]

After a short-lived boom following the first World War, the Society, like much Lancashire industry, entered on a long era of slow decline. The Manchester school of chemistry was also past its first peak. These circumstances naturally hampered any serious consideration of Dalton's work. The period too was not an auspicious one for the history of science. Abandoned as frivolous by the ever more narrowly specialist professional scientists and not yet able to command its own group of professionals, the subject languished. A further reason for the neglect of Dalton's work was the lack of concern with theories known to be "wrong" that was only too typical of philosophically aware historical enquirers between the Wars. Interest in Dalton lapsed to the antiquarian level of the presentation of busts, portraits, and pairs of spectacles to the Manchester Society and the display of its relics for the benefit of visiting eminences.[21] By 1938 some of the Dalton manuscripts had already disappeared. On 23 December 1940, the Society's house was burnt out, with the tragic loss of its unique library and almost all the remaining manuscripts and other relics.[22]

RECENT STUDIES AND CRUCIAL EVENTS

Although the majority of the Dalton documents have gone, professional historians of science, and with them new scholarly standards, have arrived. The first sign that the long era of neglect was over, was L. K. Nash's reappraisal of the origins of the chemi-

20. W. W. H. Gee, H. F. Coward, and A. Harden, "John Dalton's Lectures and Lecture Illustrations," *Manchester Memoirs 59* (1914–1915), no. 12.

21. See e.g., *Manchester Memoirs 70* (1925–1926), pp. vi–vii, and *80* (1935–1936), p. xiv.

22. Partington, *History of Chemistry*, III, 760. A "List of Articles Salvaged" is in *Manchester Memoirs 84* (1939–1941), pp. xxxiv–xxxvii. A. L. Smyth, *John Dalton. A Bibliography of Works by and about Him* (Manchester, 1966), lists the few surviving lecture manuscripts.

cal atomic theory. From a study of Dalton's published papers, and with the aid of the information in "Roscoe and Harden," Nash concluded that "the creation of the chemical atomic theory was the direct outgrowth of Dalton's search for an explanation of the differences in the solubility of various gases in water." [23] Thus the wheel has come full circle. As the first person since Wilson to examine the question from beyond the bounds of Manchester chemistry, Nash arrived at substantially the same conclusion Wilson had propounded more than a century before.

However, Nash remained significantly indebted to the studies of previous generations in one important respect. Like them, he saw Dalton's elaboration of the chemical atomic theory as a "breakthrough," as a rapid response to a crucial event. In his particular case the necessary event was three interrelated developments in the summer of 1804: Dalton's formulation of a second theory of mixed gases, his successful work on hydrocarbons, and Thomas Thomson's visit. The reasons why this crucial event will not stand up to detailed examination, any more than Meldrum's favored nitrogen oxides breakthrough or Thomson's olefiant gas story, need not be elaborated here.[24] What is of greater interest is the continuing desire to explain Dalton's work in terms of crucial events and decisive breaks. This same desire is once again apparent in Henry Guerlac's stimulating and brilliantly argued essay on Dalton's work, where Richter's table of equivalents is made the vital element.[25]

The idea of scientific breakthroughs, of bold intuitive flashes of insight, of whole new trains of thought suggested by unexpected experimental results, is of course an honored element in the mythology of science. Both scientists and laymen have found this fiction convenient. It has served a functional purpose in empha-

23. "Origin of Atomic Theory," p. 108. It should be pointed out that Nash was ignorant of Wilson's earlier study and that, thanks to the existence of Roscoe and Harden's *New View*, he was able to present a far more detailed and sophisticated account of the context of Dalton's first atomic weight measurements than was possible for Wilson.

24. See A. Thackray, "The Origin of Dalton's Chemical Atomic Theory: Daltonian Doubts Resolved," *Isis* 57 (1966), 35–55.

25. "Some Daltonian Doubts," *Isis* 52 (1961), 544–554.

sizing that creative scientific insight cannot be bought and sold like an ordinary commodity. It has also served pedagogic ends, in making the scientist seem mysterious, remote, and exciting, not a mere mechanical producer of "laws." It is not surprising that historians of Dalton's work have more often than not been under its sway. However, a more sober attention to the available facts clearly shows that Dalton's thought was evolutionary, slow to mature, and essentially consistent from youth to old age.

The need to paint him primarily as a chemist, and the desire to establish the crucial events that led to the chemical atomic theory, sociologically and historically understandable though they may be, have meant an unfortunately narrow focus on supposedly critical years. The broader context of Dalton's thought is little explored. The particular complex of assumptions he inherited is as uncertain as the true impact of his work. If fresh attention to these matters reveals that "the founder of modern chemistry" is difficult to comprehend within any traditional viewpoint, whether of chemistry or crucial events, that will be just one of history's many ironies.

4. The Life of a Natural Philosopher

*I doubt not but my inclination
would yet adapt itself to any
business that promised to be of
advantage.*
        John Dalton in 1790

QUAKER SCHOOLS AND QUAKER NETWORKS

If the provincial Dissenter of dubiously middle-class background, obscure education, and self-made opportunity is the characteristic figure of late-eighteenth-century English natural philosophy, then John Dalton is the classic example of the species. The Daltons may be traced back in west Cumberland at least to the late sixteenth century. From that time the family seems to have owned and farmed a small amount of land. However, John Dalton's father Joseph, himself a younger son, had no holding until his elder brother died without issue in 1786. The property then inherited went at Joseph's death the following year to Jonathan, his own elder son. Only when Jonathan died a bachelor in 1834 did the now considerably augmented acreage finally come to John Dalton, who by this time had independently accumulated wealth more than sufficient to his own frugal bachelor ways.[1]

In the eighteenth century, west Cumberland enjoyed considerable prosperity as a mining and trading area, with an important series of coastal ports engaged in local and overseas commerce. George Fox had earlier seen his first major evangelistic successes

1. The best source for Dalton's private life is Henry Lonsdale, *John Dalton,* The Worthies of Cumberland, no. 5 (1874). Extensive information on the landholdings of the Dalton family, including maps, wills, etc., may be found in the Dalton (Eaglesfield) Mss. in the County Record Office, Carlisle, Ref. D/Da.

in this region, whole villages and families (including the Daltons) undergoing conversion to his doctrines. The area was thus peculiarly important within the developing international life of the Society of Friends. Trading and commercial interests blended well with the social organization and ethical concerns of Fox's followers. In time strong links were formed between these northern Friends, Quaker manufacturers in the Midlands, London merchants, and Philadelphia residents. This network of connections, coupled with the sect's strong emphasis on education and the interest in natural philosophy displayed by so many of its members, is the key to understanding the peculiarly favorable context in which Dalton grew and matured as a scientific thinker.[2]

Though his father was somewhat feckless, his mother came from a more prosperous local family. John was strongly influenced by her determination and tenacity. He made rapid progress in the village school, one of the many in the area maintained and subsidized (often precariously) by the Quakers, through the agency of their regional Quarterly and annual National Meetings. Indeed, when the master withdrew and the school was about to collapse, Dalton himself took over as teacher, though barely twelve. He also quickly attracted the attention of Elihu Robinson, the most prominent among the local Friends and a naturalist of significant stature. Robinson's encouragement is reflected in the story of how John at the age of thirteen copied out verbatim an issue of the *Ladies' Diary,* a popular but by no means trivial annual devoted to mathematics and philosophy.[3]

At this time Dalton's future seemed uncertain, and he was of necessity put to work as a laborer on the local small-holdings. In 1781 he was rescued by an invitation to succeed his elder brother as assistant in a Kendal boarding school, forty miles away. Kendal

2. See E. Hughes, *Cumberland and Westmorland. 1700–1830,* North Country Life in the Eighteenth Century, no. 2 (1965); F. Nicholson and E. Axon, *The Older Nonconformity in Kendal* (Kendal, 1915); A. Raistrick, *Quakers in Science and Industry* (1950); M. Irwin, *The History of the Pardshaw Meeting and Meeting House* (1919).

3. Lonsdale, *Dalton,* p. 39. For a fuller picture of Robinson's importance in the regional and national Quaker network see ch. 2 above (esp. n. 15).

was an old established and thriving center for the region's commerce and culture. In recognition of its centrality and importance, the school to which Dalton moved had recently been rebuilt and reequipped by the Quakers.

The very existence of the school, the generosity of its staffing and facilities, and the invitation to John to replace his brother, all serve to illustrate aspects of the sect's concern that Friends be educated, a concern at once locally rooted and nationally fostered. The list of the school's benefactors was headed by John Fothergill, the London physician (and personal friend of Robinson). It also included such wealthy Midland entrepreneurs as Abraham Darby and Richard Reynolds. More immediately important than the web of contacts the benefactors' list displays is the use that the school's first principal made of the £150 available for the library. George Bewley (himself a distant cousin of Dalton) was quick to purchase not only Newton's *Principia,* but also a variety of supporting Newtonian texts. The collection was rounded out with various items of apparatus, including a "two foot reflecting telescope," "a double microscope," and (for £21) "a double barreled air pump with apparatus" (see Figure 2).[4]

Dalton did not feel such valuable resources as these worth even a mention in the account of his early life that he was later to authorize for publication.[5] Nor did he refer to the stimulus available to such a talented and enterprising youth from the continued flow of Quaker visitors. He also forgot to include the public lectures given by itinerant natural philosophers (Kendal being, inter alia, an important staging post on the coach route from London to Scotland). Typical of the courses available was that of John Banks in 1782. In a seven-week stay in Kendal, Banks offered "twelve lectures, which include the most useful, interesting

4. See Ms. Packet 98, Strong Room, Friends Meeting House, Kendal. These hitherto unknown manuscripts reveal and document the extremely high calibre of the school, revising the interesting if neglected account in J. F. Curwen, *Kirbie-Kendall* (Kendal, 1900), pp. 402–405.

5. W. C. Henry, *Memoirs of the Life and Scientific Researches of John Dalton* (1854), p. 2. See also D. I. Duveen and H. S. Klickstein, "John Dalton's Autobiography," *Journal of Chemical Education* 32 (1955), 333–334.

Nable 1773	Per contra	Cr £ s d			
June 20	By sundries brought forward	549	4	10½
	By cash paid for Hugenii Analysis Geometrica	—	1	6
	By Do for Malcolms System of Arithmetic	—	6	—
	By Do for Oughtreds Key to the Mathematics	—	—	9
	By Do for Gunter's Works	—	1	—
	By Do for Hawney's Trigonometry	—	3	6
	By Do for Hinds History of Greece	—	3	—
	By Do for Johnson's English Dictionary 2 Vols	4	10	—
	By Do for Rollins Roman History 10 Vols	3	—	—
	By Do for Pemberton's Philosophy	—	12	—
	By Do for Rutherforth's Philosophy 2 Vols	2	2	—
	By Do for Osbeck's Voyages 2 Vols	—	10	—
	By Do for Kennets Roman Antiquities	—	2	6
	By Do for Rapin's History of England 21 Vols	5	5	—
	By Do for Burnets Theory of the Earth 2 Vols	—	9	—
	By Do for Maclaurin's Algebra	—	5	—
	By Do for Cicero's Works 20 Vols	2	5	—
	By Do for Pope's Homer's Iliad 5 Vols	—	14	—
	By Do for Montague's Letters 3 Vols	—	8	—
	By Do for Rows Letters	—	1	—
	By Do for Macaulay's History of England 4 Vols	—	16	—
	By Do for the Rambler 4 Vols	—	11	—
	By Do for the Tatler 4 Vols	—	9	—
	By Do for Addison's Travels	—	2	6
	By Do for Jesuits Perspective	—	10	6
	By Do for Gunter's Quadrant	—	5	—
	By Do for a two Foot reflecting Telescope	12	12	—
	By Do for a double barrell'd Air Pump with Apparatus	21	—	—
	By Do for a double Microscope with Do	6	6	—
	By Do for Hadley's Quadrant	1	16	—
	By Do for Theodolite with Telescope &c	10	10	—
	By Do for Carriage of Books & Instruments	2	3	8
		627	5	9¾

2. The Account Book of Kendal Friends School. Some of the books and apparatus purchased in 1775. (Courtesy of the Kendal Meeting of the Society of Friends.)

and popular parts of philosophy," the lectures being illustrated by extensive apparatus.[6] Despite his failure to acknowledge their influence, Dalton obviously modelled his own subsequent public courses on lectures such as these.

What Dalton did acknowledge was the presumably still greater stimulus he found in the library, learning, and enthusiasm of another Kendal Quaker—John Gough, the blind natural philosopher of Wordsworth's *Excursion*. As Dalton explained in a 1783 letter to Peter Crosthwaite, a Keswick Friend and fellow naturalist: "John Gough is . . . a perfect master of the Latin, Greek, and French tongues . . . Under his tuition, I have since acquired a good knowledge of them. He understands well all the different branches of mathematics . . . He knows by the touch, taste and smell, almost every plant within twenty miles of this place . . . He is a good proficient in astronomy, chemistry, medicine, etc. . . . He has the advantage of all the books he has a mind for . . . He and I have been for a long time very intimate; as our pursuits are common—viz, mathematical and philosophical." [7]

Under Gough's tuition, Dalton made rapid progress in mathematics, meteorology, and botany. He began to keep daily meteorological records, in emulation of his master. These were steadfastly continued from 1787 till the day he died. He started to compile a *Hortus Siccus*. It filled eleven volumes by the time of his final entries, in 1829.[8] As a "teacher of the mathematics in Kendal" he also enjoyed an increasing reputation for his successes in the yearly puzzles and prize competitions of the *Ladies'* and *Gentleman's Diaries*.[9] Rooted in such a national complex of educational institutions and social contacts favorably disposed to his

6. *Cumberland Pacquet and Ware's Whitehaven Advertiser,* 28 October 1782. Banks was also a significant figure on the Manchester scene. See A. E. Musson and E. Robinson, *Science and Technology in the Industrial Revolution* (Manchester, 1969), pp. 107–108. See also ch. 2 above, esp. n. 21.

7. Part of the letter is reproduced in Henry, *Memoirs of Dalton*, pp. 9–10. See also the further remarks on Gough in the preface to J. Dalton, *Meteorological Observations and Essays*, 2nd ed. (Manchester, 1834).

8. See R. S. Adamson and A. McK. Crabtree, "The Herbarium of John Dalton," *Manchester Memoirs 63* (1918–1919), no. 1. See also ch. 7, n. 10 below.

9. See T. T. Wilkinson, "An Account of the Early Mathematical and Philosophical Writings of the Late Dr. Dalton," *Manchester Memoirs 17* (1855), 1–30.

taste for natural philosophy, a man of lesser ambition and ability might have known contentment. Not John Dalton.

In 1785 George Bewley withdrew from the Kendal school. Jonathan and John Dalton thereupon took over as joint principals, and their sister Mary moved from Eaglesfield to become housekeeper.[10] Despite his increased responsibilities at the school, John was soon offering his own first series of public lectures in Kendal. These lectures treated mechanics, optics, pneumatics, astronomy, and the use of the globes, with the aid of the school's apparatus.[11] Even with such new outlets for his energy and curiosity, John was obviously becoming restless within the confines of a local scientific community whose lessons he had mastered and whose possibilities he had so fully explored. In 1790 he wrote to Bewley, Robinson, and his uncle Thomas Greenup (a London barrister) to seek advice on his prospects in medicine and law (the Society of Friends having no clergy).

Dalton argued that "very few people of middling genius, or capacity for other business" become schoolmasters. His own desire for a profession with an "expectation of greater emolument" led to his queries, especially about the feasibility of studying medicine at Edinburgh. The replies were not enthusiastic. Greenup in particular chose to say that medicine and law were "totally out of the reach of a person in thy circumstances" and that Dalton should aim at moving in the humbler sphere of apothecary or attorney where with a little capital and great industry he might, perhaps, be able to establish himself.[12] Despite this discouragement, such an ambitious and talented young man was not to be confined to a Kendal school.

In 1791 Dalton again offered a public lecture course. In 1792 he paid his first visit to London, ostensibly for the annual meeting of the Society of Friends. Shortly afterwards he was appointed professor of mathematics and natural philosophy in the "Acad-

10. Lonsdale, *Dalton*, p. 46.
11. *Ibid.*, p. 49. The extant manuscripts (n. 4 above) show that 7s-1d was spent to repair the apparatus, a month before the October 1787 lectures.
12. The letters are reproduced in Lonsdale, *Dalton*, pp. 74–77.

emy" or "New College" which Socinian- and Unitarian-oriented Dissenters had recently established in the rapidly expanding town of Manchester, following the demise of the nearby Warrington Academy at which Joseph Priestley had once taught.[13] If Quaker beliefs in literacy, education, and communion with God through his works had served to orient Dalton's interests, the limited opportunities within the schools maintained by the sect could not contain his energies. Instead, the network of contacts they provided proved his stepping-stone to greater opportunities. Medicine, law, indeed "any business that promised to be of advantage" were what he sought. And though neither he nor anyone else could yet see it clearly, the career in science for which he had to settle was in process of becoming just that promising business for which he yearned.

EARLY DAYS IN MANCHESTER

Initially, Dalton seems to have been well pleased with his appointment at Manchester Academy. Reporting on the situation to Elihu Robinson, his early patron, he explained how "there is in this town a large library [Chetham's], furnished with the best books in every art, science and language, which is open to all *gratis;* when thou art apprised of this and such like circumstances, thou considerest me in my private apartments, undisturbed, having a good fire, and a philosophical apparatus around me, thou wilt be able to form an opinion whether I spend my time in slothful inactivity of body and mind." Despite the availability of library and apparatus, teaching duties seem to have absorbed John's energies in his early years in Manchester. Called upon to

13. While in London, Dalton stayed with Greenup, his barrister-uncle. They no doubt further explored Dalton's ambitions. See E. M. Brockbank, *John Dalton. Some Unpublished Letters* (Manchester, 1944). Of the 80 students admitted to the New College in 1786–1792, 6 came from Kendal and 6 from other parts of the Lake District [see *Roll of Students Entered at Manchester College* (Manchester, 1862).] Dalton's teaching was thus presumably known to its Trustees, as well as his emerging reputation as a minor natural philosopher. The early days of the College are cursorily discussed in V. D. Davis, *A History of Manchester College* (Allen and Unwin, 1932).

offer college-level mathematics and natural philosophy for the first time, he soon found himself expected to cover chemistry as well. As he ruefully noted, it was "often expedient to prepare my lectures previously." In addition there was the necessary "attendance upon students 21 hours in the week." [14] Walking tours in the summer vacation, regular local and occasional regional Quaker meetings, return visits to his beloved Lake District and, in 1796, a further set of Kendal lectures served to more than fill out the remaining time.

If Dalton was secure and confident in this new life, his employers were not. Beset by the pressures of war and political reaction, the Manchester Academy lurched from crisis to crisis throughout the 1790's. The other two chairs (theology and classics) saw a succession of incumbents, each less distinguished and enduring than the last. Dalton was soon senior professor, in fact if not name. On 26 March 1800 he too announced his intention to resign his teaching position at the close of the session, for immediate reasons that remain obscure. Perhaps he was dissatisfied with the college's radical posture, perhaps unsettled by its faculty changes and uncertain future, perhaps unhappy that he remained the lowest paid of the three professors (eventually receiving £52–10–0 annual salary, plus approximately £50 in fees), perhaps quite simply confident in his popularity and teaching abilities. The stormy path of the Academy, and the way that "Quaker Dalton" was always peripheral to the deepest concerns of its Unitarian leaders, may be followed in the manuscript minutes of the institution.[15] These minutes also reveal the interlocking leadership of the college and the Literary and Philosophical Society. Dalton's ability to reject the one organization, while rising steadily in the other, says much about his tact and quiet determination.

In September 1800, the *Manchester Mercury* advertised the opening of his own "Mathematical Academy," offering tuition in mathematics, experimental philosophy, and chemistry (see Figure

14. Lonsdale, *Dalton*, p. 98.
15. See the volume of "Minutes of the Proceedings of Manchester Academy" now preserved at Manchester College, Oxford (the Academy's lineal descendant).

Mathematical Academy, Manchester.

JOHN DALTON, Secretary to the Literary and Philosophical Society, and late Mathematical Tutor at the New College, Manchester, respectfully informs his Friends and the Public, that he intends shortly to open a MATHEMATICAL and PHILO-SOPHICAL ACADEMY in Manchester.

The course of instruction will comprise Arithmetic, Merchants' Accounts, Geography and the use of the Globes, the Mathematics and Natural Philosophy:— Also the Theory of Language and Universal Grammar.

An annual Course of Lectures on Experimental Philosophy and Chemistry will be given, illustrated by an extensive apparatus.

Young Gentlemen above fourteen years of age will be admissible.

Terms—Ten Guineas per annum.

Two vacations in the year, together not exceeding two months.

N.B. Application may be made to him, at No. 35, Falkner-street.

August 30, 1800.

3. An Advertisement for Dalton's Mathematical Academy. From the *Manchester Mercury*, 2 September 1800. (Courtesy of the Manchester Public Libraries.)

3). Despite competition from other private teachers in the town, success came quickly. Within two years Dalton could drily observe that "my Academy has done very well for me hitherto. I have about eight or nine day pupils at a medium, at ten guineas per annum, and am now giving upwards of twenty lessons per week, privately, at two shillings each besides. I am not yet rich enough to retire, notwithstanding." [16] Private teaching of this fashion more than adequately supported him for the rest of his

16. From a 22 March 1802 letter to Elihu Robinson, reproduced in Lonsdale, *Dalton*, p. 153.

days. Far from being regarded as a degrading chore, such activity was common to those many Dissenters whose academies and popular lectures formed one of the major strengths of English science throughout this period of embryonic professionalization. Self-help, private initiative, technological curiosity, and belief in natural knowledge as a cultural mode were characteristics of that particular strand of Industrial Revolution science which is both exemplified by John Dalton's work and encapsulated by his lifetime.

When he moved from Kendal to Manchester, John Dalton also entered a far wider and more demanding scientific world. Indicative of new horizons and new opportunities was his 13 October 1794 election to membership in the Manchester Literary and Philosophical Society, a Society then in its first great productive epoch, and one to which Dalton was himself to contribute so substantially. His sponsors were Thomas Henry (translator of Lavoisier's *Opuscules*), Thomas Percival (pioneer sanitary reformer and medical statistician), and Robert Owen (entrepreneur and visionary protosocialist).[17] Within a month of his election, Dalton was reading to the Society his first major scientific paper, on some "Extraordinary facts relating to the vision of colours, with observations."

The paper is an excellent example of that careful observation, bold theorizing, and dogmatic belief which together characterize Dalton's work. The paper provided the first systematic notice and attempted explanation of the existence of color blindness, a defect which John shared with his brother Jonathan. Collecting information from other people similarly afflicted, he was able to give a careful account of the actual phenomenon. Dalton's explanation of his own failure to see red was in terms of the supposed blue, that is, red-ray absorbing, nature of the aqueous medium of his eye. (Characteristically, he refused to entertain Thomas Young's later alternative explanation. He even went so far as to instruct that his own eye be dissected after death to confirm his hypothe-

17. R. A. Smith, *Memoir of John Dalton and History of the Atomic Theory up to his Time* [*Manchester Memoirs 18*] (1856), 27.

sis. The dissection was duly undertaken, with the opposite result.) If the theory now seems inadequate, the meticulous detail and bold speculations on an important and neglected phenomenon were enough to establish the newly elected member's place in the front ranks of Manchester's burgeoning group of natural philosophers.

In contrast to this brilliant early investigation, Dalton's other major scientific achievements present many puzzling problems of chronology and interpretation. What is clear is that within five years of leaving Manchester Academy and setting up as an independent teacher, Dalton had completed in essential outline the work on which his major and enduring scientific reputation was to rest. These years saw the law of gaseous expansion at constant pressure (also called Charles's Law after its independent and earlier French discoverer), the law of partial pressures in gaseous systems, and the chemical atomic theory (which for the first time gave significance to, and provided a technique for calculating, the relative weights of the ultimate particles of all known chemicals, whether elements or compounds).[18]

Despite this brilliant efflorescence of creative thought, Dalton's achievements can be properly appreciated only when seen against the background of his earlier research and writing. Yet that background and Dalton's own scientific formation are ill understood. It is clear that previously accepted accounts, with their straight line of development from Isaac Newton's speculations on the fundamental particles of matter in the 31st Query of the *Opticks* to John Dalton's chemical atomic theory a century later, are woefully inadequate.[19] Their replacement by a more careful, convincing narrative is not entirely possible. Here it is germane to stress how easily Dalton took to Manchester life and what intellectual stimulus and financial opportunity were offered to the new man of science by this prototypical city and the Industrial Revolution

18. These developments may be followed in Henry, *Memoirs of Dalton*, chs. 2 and 3; and most recently in D. S. L. Cardwell, ed., *John Dalton and the Progress of Science* (Manchester, 1968), *passim*.

19. See A. Thackray, *Atoms and Powers: An Essay on Newtonian Matter-Theory and the Development of Chemistry* (Cambridge, Mass., 1970), esp. chs. 3 and 6.

it exemplified. Dalton's role in the Literary and Philosophical Society, his activity in other groups, his civil recognition, his public lectures, and his changing place in the mythology of science all reflect different lights on the professionalization of the scientific enterprise.

THE INDUSTRIAL REVOLUTION MAN OF SCIENCE

The Manchester Literary and Philosophical Society was founded in 1781. The first, it was also the foremost of the rash of such societies founded in the growing manufacturing centers of England as the Industrial Revolution progressed. The hopes, needs, and social aspirations that led to the creation of these new groups are still unexplored. What is now most often remembered of the Manchester Society is the way it nourished creative science of the highest calibre, of which John Dalton's work is the best known but by no means solitary example. Although Dalton was ultimately to bring great prestige to the Society, the Society in its turn played an early and critical role in his intellectual development.

The "Lit and Phil" offered legitimation, audience, encouragement, and reward to the scientific practitioner at a time when science still enjoyed little public recognition as a *profession*. Not only did the Society provide an extensive and up-to-date library, a vehicle of publication (the *Manchester Memoirs,* which were eventually to contain 26 of the 117 papers Dalton read before the "Lit and Phil"), and, from 1800, a home for Dalton's apparatus and experimental labors. It also offered critical encouragement and personal reward. This last may be seen objectified and institutionalized in John's path through member of the Committee of Papers, to secretary, to vice-president (1808), and finally to president (1817). In that capacity he ruled the Society firmly but efficiently for the remaining twenty-seven years of his life (see Figure 4).[20]

20. There is no satisfactory history of the Society, but see R. A. Smith, *A Centenary of Science in Manchester* [*Manchester Memoirs* 29] (1873).

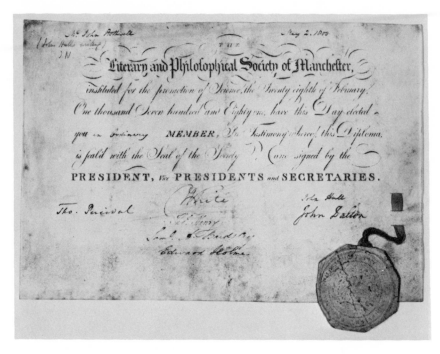

4. A Membership Certificate for the Manchester Literary and Philosophical Society. (Property of the author.)

If the Manchester group provided the essential environment for the flowering of Dalton's abilities, other scientific societies were more peripheral to his life. Dalton showed considerable reluctance to be a candidate for election to the Royal Society of London. In 1810 he rebuffed Humphry Davy's approaches, and he was finally elected in 1822 only when some friends proposed him without his knowledge. It was not till 1826 that he submitted the first of only four papers to that body. Though awarded one of the initial two Royal Medals in that same year, in recognition of the chemical atomic theory, he appears to have been almost completely indifferent to the Society's affairs. This indifference reflects in part the gulf in social class and professional stance between the provincial teacher committed to his science and the still largely amateur, cosmopolitan, and dilettante-oriented Royal Society. Dalton's attitude may also be seen in his comment to

Charles Babbage that if the latter's reformist 1830 tract on *The Decline of Science in England* "should stimulate the officers and other active members of the Royal Society to the performance of their duties, it may be of essential service to the promotion of science." Only in 1834, when he himself was at last enjoying widespread social recognition as the archetype of the dedicated and successful man of science, did Dalton finally make his formal bow at the Society.[21]

A sharp contrast appears between John Dalton's attitude to the Royal Society and his response to other groups whose socializing functions were more clearly subordinated to the recognition of professional merit and the promotion and dissemination of science. Thus, in 1816 he willingly accepted his election as a corresponding member of the French *Académie des Sciences*. In 1822 he even went so far as to visit Paris, where he "had the happiness to know" such preeminent men of science as P. S. Laplace, C. L. Berthollet, J. L. Gay-Lussac, L. J. Thenard, F. J. D. Arago, G. L. Cuvier, A. L. Breguet, P. L. Dulong, and A. M. Ampère. During this visit he took his seat at a meeting of the *Académie,* being introduced by Gay-Lussac, then president. He also dined at Arcueil with the members of Berthollet's informal but influential scientific school. In 1830 he enjoyed the further honor of being elected one of the eight Foreign Associates of the *Académie.*[22]

An even clearer case of Dalton's willing involvement with serious scientific endeavor is seen in his attitude to the British Association for the Advancement of Science. One of the few men of scientific distinction present at the 1831 foundation meeting in York, he played an active role in the Association's affairs. He chaired the "chemistry, mineralogy, electricity and magnetism" committee in 1832; was a vice-president of the Association and

21. Dalton visited London that spring to sit for his statue by the fashionable sculptor Chantrey. He was also presented at Court. On 1 May 1834 he signed the Charter Book and was admitted to the Royal Society, it being drily noted in the Society's *Journal Book* that he was "some time since elected." See also letter 22 in ch. 7 below and ch. 2 above.

22, Henry, *Memoirs of Dalton,* pp. 163–168; and see M. P. Crosland, *The Society of Arcueil* (Heinemann, 1967), pp. 417–420 ff. See also ch. 7 below, letters 16a and 23a.

chairman of the chemistry section in 1833; in 1834 was deputy chairman; and in 1835 vice-president of the chemistry and mineralogy committee. In 1836 he was vice-president of the chemistry section and again became a vice-president-elect of the Association. This activity was abruptly halted by two severe paralytic attacks in April 1837. The attacks left Dalton a semi-invalid for the rest of his days, unable to undertake the strenuous traveling necessary to follow the Association in its journeyings. When the annual meeting came to Manchester in 1842, he was too feeble to take on the role of president. However, the sentiments expressed at that time, and the presidential address that followed his death in 1844, leave no doubt as to Dalton's importance within the early life of the Association. His involvement clearly illustrates one way in which England's emerging group of committed scientists was seeking to create and consolidate the institutional forms their professional life demanded.[23]

If Dalton in old age enjoyed widespread recognition and honor, he also knew a rather different public role throughout his life. His early lecture series in Kendal were in the tradition of those broadly popular performances by itinerant teachers of natural philosophy, the importance of which to the developing structure of British science has yet to be fully appreciated. The 1803 lectures at the Royal Institution were of similar type, though following more closely Dalton's special interests. Later courses were sometimes directly based on his own immediate research interests. This change indicates the growing sophistication and specialist expertise of the potential audience. The range and importance of this aspect of Dalton's work may be seen from a (probably incomplete) listing of these later courses: Manchester in 1805 and 1806, Edinburgh and Glasgow in 1807, Manchester in 1808, London in

23. The early years of the British Association would repay careful study. The account in O. R. Howarth, *The British Association for the Advancement of Science. A Retrospect* (British Association, 1931), is disappointingly sketchy. Dalton's intimate involvement can only be deduced by scrutinizing the *Annual Reports* of the Association, and from surviving correspondence. Thus Charles Babbage urged that the 1833 meeting be held in Manchester, not Cambridge, in part as "a fit respect to Dalton" (28 April 1832 letter to C. G. B. Daubeny, in Magdalen College, Oxford, Mss. 400, item 2). See also chs. 6 and 7 below.

1810, Manchester in 1811 and 1814, Birmingham in 1817, Manchester in 1820, Leeds in 1823, Birmingham in 1825 and Manchester in 1825, 1827, 1828, 1829, 1834, and 1835. For a number of years from 1825 he was also lecturer in pharmaceutical chemistry for Thomas Turner's Pine Street School of Medicine and Surgery. Among other things these varied lecture courses added substantially to Dalton's income. For instance, the Royal Institution paid him 80 guineas in 1803, while his 1806 Manchester lectures showed a profit of £58–2–0.[24]

With such an extensive repertoire in addition to his teaching and research, Dalton over the years built up a substantial collection of apparatus. If his predilection was for bold generalizations and elegantly simple experimental tests, he had a considerable range of equipment available, whether in Kendal, at the Manchester New College, or in his laboratory at the Literary and Philosophical Society. In addition, he knew that success as a public lecturer demanded adequate demonstrations. Thus on one visit to London alone (in 1805) he spent £200 on apparatus. The young Benjamin Silliman, while on his first European tour, expressed a suitable awe at the elaborate experiments accompanying Dalton's subsequent Manchester lectures.[25]

Many writers on Dalton have exaggerated the supposed poverty of his training and his lack of laboratory equipment. In so doing they have failed to display an adequate historical sympathy. The point is not the crudity of Dalton's resources when measured against some later more affluent standard but the entrepreneurial processes by which the new men of Industrial Revolution science accumulated the "capital" of apparatus necessary to scientific business. In his ability first to make his own meteorological instruments, then to utilise and exploit the equipment of schools, colleges, and scientific societies, and finally to procure his own stock

24. The best account of Dalton's lecture courses is W. W. H. Gee, H. F. Coward and A. Harden, "John Dalton's Lectures and Lecture Illustrations," *Manchester Memoirs* 59 (1914–1915), no. 12. See also E. M. Brockbank, *The Foundation of Provincial Medical Education in England and of the Manchester School in Particular* (Manchester, Manchester University Press, 1936), pp. 75–76.

25. G. P. Fisher, *Life of Benjamin Silliman* (Philadelphia, 1866), I, 138–140.

in trade, Dalton exemplifies a pattern repeated time and again at this period. Such private enterprise in the creation of research laboratories was characteristic of both the style and vitality of British science at this time, despite the lack of more formal and ponderous institutional provisions on the French model.

The oft-told story of Dalton's contempt for books would seem even more misplaced. His early acquaintance with John Gough, the facilities of the Kendal school, and his eager appreciation of Manchester's libraries all speak of his thirst for and appreciation of a wide range of knowledge and information. The sale catalog of his belongings confirms the picture.[26] In all these ways—lectures, apparatus, books—Dalton reveals the incipient professionalism of a new class in English science. Without the benefit of Oxford, Cambridge, or medicine, from which natural knowledge had previously drawn its English devotees, such men as he could not afford a casual or dilettante attitude toward their work. His livelihood and entrée to more rewarding social circles depended too acutely on that mixture of entrepreneurial talent and professional scientific competence which one may also see displayed in the careers of Humphry Davy and Michael Faraday.

If his public activity knew no tumultuous crises, John Dalton's private life was even more unruffled. As an active and ambitious youth he had little free time. His Kendal thoughts on trying medicine or law were encouraged by the knowledge that the emoluments of a Quaker schoolmaster "are not sufficient to support a small family with the decency and reputation I could wish." By 1794 he was saying instead that "my head is too full of triangles, chemical processes, and electrical experiments, etc., to think much of marriage." [27] Lacking a wife and family of his own, John was deeply attached to several relatives and associates. His brother Jonathan, William Henry, Peter Ewart, and, latterly, Peter Clare were among his closest friends. In addition his fre-

26. See *The Late Dr. Dalton's Effects* (Manchester Central Library, Tract H 93), and ch. 2 above.

27. From an 8 April 1790 letter to Elihu Robinson, reproduced in Lonsdale, *Dalton*, pp. 74 and 129.

quent walking tours, lecture trips, and visits to Quaker meetings made him known to a wide circle, though his quiet and reserved personal manner was often mistaken for indifference or uncouthness by strangers, especially in his later years.[28]

When Dalton died in July 1844, he was accorded a civic funeral with full honors. His body first lay in state in Manchester Town Hall for four days while more than 40,000 people filed past his coffin. The funeral procession included representatives of the city's major political, commercial, and scientific bodies, shops and offices being closed for the day as a mark of respect.[29] This attention was in part a display of civic pride by what in his lifetime had become the pre-eminent provincial city. It was also a vivid demonstration of the growth and change that had occurred in the cultural place and social functions of natural knowledge, in Dalton's lifetime.

In 1766 provincial scientific enquiry was in the hands of little groups of devotees, scattered and remote in villages and small towns. By 1844 science "had fixed itself in Lancashire" (among other places). In so doing, it had assumed new forms and purposes in response to an urban, industrial environment which was itself equally new. Science and progress together became part of Manchester's self-image, and John Dalton a correspondingly important reference point. There was exaggeration and confusion, but also truth, in the contemporary belief that "with respect to science, the whole phenomenon of Manchester society is but a continual series of investigations into, and practical applications of, scientific knowledge." The same commentator continued that "when Manchester ceases to honour science, science will cease to honour it. There is little room for wonder then, that science is held in respect, or that the funeral of the late Dr. Dalton afforded

28. For a typically exaggerated account, see Lonsdale, *Dalton*, pp. 246–247. In sharp contrast is W. Henry's warning of how this reserved manner of Dalton's was mistaken by strangers. In the same letter, Henry makes clear Dalton's "love of honourable fame." See Henry to C. G. B. Daubeny, 30 Aug. 1831. Magdalen College, Oxford. Mss. 400, item 14. I am indebted to Dr. W. V. Farrar for drawing this letter to my attention.

29. See "Lying in State and Funeral of the Late Dr. Dalton," *Illustrated London News*, 17 August 1844.

a spectacle of homage paid to departed genius by the public bodies of the town." [30]

Such a spectacle of homage was at once an appropriate and an
incongruous climax to Dalton's life. Its pomp and circumstance
offended Quaker canons and contrasted sharply with the under-
stated manner of his days. On the other hand, the formal linking
of Dalton's fame with the new status Manchester had achieved in
his lifetime provides a rich symbol of those real, if subtle, reciprocal relations between science and the Industrial Revolution
which find their classic expression in John Dalton's career.

30. From the translator's commentary in M. Leon Faucher, *Manchester in 1844;
Its Present Condition and Future Prospects* (1844), pp. 21–22.

5. A New System of Chemical Philosophy

*[My] new view of the first principles
or elements of bodies and their combinations . . . will produce the most important changes in the system of chemistry, and reduce the whole to a science
of great simplicity.*

John Dalton in 1807

THE PROBLEM OUTLINED

The slow emergence of Dalton's chemical atomic theory has long
been a considerable puzzle to historians of science. The lengthy
delay between Dalton's work on mixed gases (September 1801) or
particle weights (September 1803) and the publication of his *New
System of Chemical Philosophy* (June 1808) has called forth a variety of explanations. It is now more than half a century since A. N.
Meldrum stressed "the efforts Dalton had to make, in order to
arouse attention to the importance of his ideas regarding atoms."
Amplifying this position, Meldrum argued that "for some nine
years (1801–1810), if not longer, he endeavoured to spread abroad
his ideas, both by private communications and publicly, by his
writings and by lectures in various parts of the country . . . Dalton's chemical theory was formed by the 6th September 1803, and
he proceeded forthwith to extend and apply it, and make it
known in every direction." [1] This view of events has long since
lost its appeal. However it has not yet been replaced by any systematic and detailed account of Dalton's thought and action during those critical years. The aim of this chapter is to give just

1. A. N. Meldrum's series of papers on "The Development of the Atomic
Theory" appeared in the *Manchester Memoirs* between 1909 and 1911. They re-
main an important study of the issues involved. The quotation is from *Manchester
Memoirs* 55 (1910–1911), no. 19, pp. 2, 3.

such an account. To do so it will be necessary to utilize previously unexamined manuscripts (some of which are reproduced in Chapter 6), unexploited material in printed sources, and the results of several recent scholarly enquiries into Dalton's work.[2]

Discussion of chemical atomic theory has often been confused by a myth. This myth pictures Dalton as the first to appreciate that different species of chemical are composed of particles of specifically differing weights. There is a further, closely allied source of confusion. It is to overemphasize the *atomic* part of Dalton's theory and to see him as everywhere insisting on *unsplittable chemical atoms*.[3] Instead, it should be clearly realized how the idea that ultimate particles of different chemicals differ in weight was common to chemists of the period and not original to Dalton. And initially at least he used the term "atom" not in the radical sense it came to possess but rather in its other common meaning of *smallest unit possessing a given nature*. Thus Dalton's achievement was not the creation of a new system of "chemical atomic weights" which had to battle against an entrenched system of atoms of the same weight, as many textbooks suppose. His great accomplishment was rather *the establishment of valid rules of chemical combination and the realization of the utility of relative particle weights*. Once this has been appreciated, and the picture of Dalton as self-conscious inventor of the chemical atomic theory discarded, many of the questions surrounding his statements and activities from 1801 to 1808 disappear. The truth is that it was Dalton's own slow realization of the chemical importance of parti-

2. See L. K. Nash, "The Origin of Dalton's Chemical Atomic Theory," *Isis* 47 (1956), 101–116; H. E. Guerlac, "Some Daltonian Doubts," *Isis* 52 (1961), 544–554; R. Siegfried, "Further Daltonian Doubts," *Isis* 54 (1963), 480–481; A. Thackray, "Daltonian Doubts Resolved," *Isis* 57 (1966), 35–55; S. Mauskopf, "Thomson before Dalton," *Annals of Science* 25 (1969), 229–242; and "Daltonian Doubts Exhumed," *Ambix* 17 (1970), 182–191. See also J. R. Partington, *A History of Chemistry*, III (MacMillan, 1962), 749–822; F. Greenaway, *John Dalton and the Atom* (1966); E. Patterson, *John Dalton and the Atomic Theory* (New York, 1970). Earlier discussions may be followed with the aid of A. L. Smyth, *John Dalton. A Bibliography of Works by and about Him* (Manchester, 1966), while a synoptic view of recent scholarship is available in the 1966 conference proceedings, *John Dalton and the Progress of Science*, ed. D. S. L. Cardwell (Manchester, 1968).

3. See, e.g., the statement in Partington, *History*, III, 784.

cle weights which made his accounts of the origins of his theory so unsatisfactory to historians intent on seeing a "discovery."

To Meldrum "Dalton was simply deficient in historical instinct . . . [he] never had in his mind a precise view of how the theory developed, and when invited to give one he produced, on the spur of the moment, an account to which he did, or did not, adhere on the next occasion." [4] Meldrum notwithstanding, the various accounts Dalton gave agree nicely with the pattern of activity that can now be reconstructed from the available materials. All the extant evidence confirms the strict historical accuracy of the information in Dalton's own written statements. Therefore one thesis of this chapter is that *Dalton himself provides the most satisfactory guide to his own activities.* Confusion only arises when uncritical confidence is given to the reports of other witnesses as to what he said and did. (Admittedly there are real, though somewhat different, problems associated with Dalton's own deliberate silences and his later systematic deprecation of aspects of his early life. Again, confidence in the reliability of Dalton's statements as to the chronology and sequence of ideas and experiments does not imply a blindness to his habit of altering papers between their actual reading and subsequent publication in the *Manchester Memoirs.* As secretary of the Literary and Philosophical Society he made frequent use of his prerogative and brought his work up to date before publication, as will become apparent.)

The second thesis of this chapter is that *it was by a gradual, internal process that Dalton's thought developed.* Hence in discussions of the emergence of the chemical atomic theory, distortions occur whenever crucial significance is attributed to any one particular event—whether it be Dalton's 1804 work on marsh gas, his earlier experiments with the nitrogen oxides, the discovery of Henry's Law, the visit of Thomas Thomson, or the publication of Richter's table of equivalents. How excessive concentration on each of these events in turn has contributed to the evolving confusion over Dalton's work has been explored above. Here it is necessary, instead, to follow Dalton pursuing his particular inter-

4. *Manchester Memoirs* 55 (1910–1911), no. 3, p. 12.

ests, developing his own ideas, and finally stating a system which, though not born out of chemical enquiries, was yet to alter profoundly the course of chemical research and debate.

DALTON'S PRE-1801 CHEMICAL KNOWLEDGE

In order to understand Dalton's behavior over the years 1801–1808, it will be helpful to consider first the extent of his chemical knowledge at the start of this period. Though the subject had never been central to his concerns, he had by this time a wider knowledge of and interest in chemistry than has sometimes been realized.

Dalton's earliest mention of chemistry came when he was twenty-two, in a 12 April 1788 letter about John Gough, the blind natural philosopher whose friendship and assistance was so important in encouraging and directing his scientific concerns. Gough's collection of books was one source of his continuing education. Dalton also made good use of the impressive library of the Kendal boarding school at which he then taught. It was there that he became acquainted with Robert Boyle's researches, the school having purchased a set of Boyle's *Works* for £7–10–0, some three months after his arrival. By 1790 he could write that "with regard to chemistry, I sometime since perused Boerhaave's treatise, which I suppose is a capital one, making allowance for the time since it was written; also the *Chemical Essays* of the present Bishop of Llandaff which are a good introduction. I have likewise read Boyle's chemical tracts, but his style is so tedious and verbose that one cannot reap the full advantage from them, except they were condensed and digested a little better." [5] The acquaintance with Boerhaave may well explain the inclusion of "Fire" among the subjects treated in the otherwise mechanics-oriented course of public lectures Dalton gave in Kendal in 1791.

5. From a 25 April 1790 letter to George Bewley, quoted in E. M. Brockbank, *John Dalton. Experimental Physiologist and Would-be Physician* (Manchester, 1929), pp. 6–7. See also W. C. Henry, *Memoirs of the Life and Scientific Researches of John Dalton* (1854), pp. 9–10; and Ms. packet 98, Strong Room, Friends Meeting House, Kendal.

Dalton's 1793 removal to be "Professor of Mathematics and Natural Philosophy, At the New College, Manchester" and his subsequent election to membership in the Manchester Literary and Philosophical Society considerably widened his scientific acquaintance. It was at this time that he met William Henry.[6] Henry was soon to become an intimate friend, attend Edinburgh University chemistry lectures, and play a vital part in provoking the first particle weight studies. It was in Manchester too that Dalton heard his first formal course on chemistry. In 1796 Dr. Garnett of Harrogate visited the town and offered a series of thirty lectures on chemical subjects. Dalton attended. Ever quick to see an opportunity, he wrote his brother in June of that same year to say "I have had some thoughts of delivering a course of lectures at Kendal this summer . . . About six lectures on chemistry and six on the other branches would be my plan." The course was duly delivered, and notes of the expenses and receipts are still preserved.[7]

Chemistry was soon added to the subjects Dalton had to teach at New College. Apparently he was equal to the challenge, for a 1797 college report says that "in the province of mathematics, natural philosophy, and chemistry, Mr Dalton has uniformly acquitted himself to the entire satisfaction of the trustees, and has been happy in possessing the respect and attachment of his pupils." The College prospectus for the following year shows his responsibilities further widened to "Mathematics and Geography, Natural Philosophy and Chemistry, theoretical and experimental." [8] Fi-

6. (1744–1836). F. R. S., manufacturing chemist, and widely respected Manchester figure. Dalton's own description of his Manchester position appears on the title page of his 1793 *Meteorological Observations and Essays*.

7. The letter is quoted in Henry, *Memoirs of Dalton*, p. 47; see also p. 11 of Dalton's notebook of "Expenses of Journeys," in the possession of the Manchester Literary and Philosophical Society. Thomas Garnett (1766–1802) was Dalton's exact contemporary and another north country "new man" of science. He was to be successively professor at Anderson's Institution, Glasgow, and the Royal Institution, London.

8. H. E. Roscoe, *John Dalton and the Rise of Modern Chemistry* (1895), p. 51; H. McLachlan, "John Dalton and Manchester," *Manchester Memoirs 86* (1945), 170. Both writers fail to point out that these statements sprang as much from the Trustees' need to placate their professor and revive sagging public confidence, as from sincere conviction and rational policy. See ch. 4 above.

nally, notice may be taken of the "catalogue of books etc." Dalton made in September 1800. This shows him owning Nicholson's, Lavoisier's and Chaptal's chemistries, as well as chemical apparatus valued at £6–14–3.[9] Thus although meteorology, mathematics, and mechanics were still the central areas of Dalton's concern in 1800, his stock of chemical knowledge and ability was by no means trivial. Certainly his formal training compares unfavorably with the German Ph.D. of 1850. It is just as certain, though far less obvious, that the patterns by which he acquired information, books, apparatus, research problems, and the confidence of colleagues were such that he automatically commanded the attention of the chemical community when chemical questions became the focus of his research.

METEOROLOGICAL CONCERNS

Though not a Newtonian in any simple sense, Dalton was deeply indebted to the British tradition of textbook and popular Newtonianism, pervasive throughout the later eighteenth century. This tradition, at once empirical and speculative, placed great stress on the uniformity (inertial homogeneity) and "internal structure" of matter and the role in nature of those short-range attractive and repulsive forces everywhere associated with (if not necessarily inherent properties of) that matter. In the hands of more sophisticated thinkers, the path from homogeneity, internal structure, and short-range forces gradually led through the "nut-shell" view of matter elaborated by Newton's immediate disciples, to the subtle curves of the Abbé Boscovich, and the "materialistic" immaterialism of Joseph Priestley.[10] Scottish commonsense philosophy provided one possible answer to the doubts

---

9. Dalton's account book for 1794–1803 is in the possession of the Manchester Literary and Philosophical Society. It contains regular catalogues of his possessions, taken on the eve of his birthday. That of 5 September 1800 details a library of 53 works, 16 being "philosophical," 15 "mathematical" and 22 "literary." On Dalton's reading habits, see also ch. 2 above.

10. See A. Thackray, *Atoms and Powers: An Essay on Newtonian Matter-Theory and the Development of Chemistry* (Cambridge, Mass., 1970), *passim*.

and paradoxes thus arrived at, although some more conservative and evangelical thinkers turned instead to the heterogeneous matter, indivisible atoms, and etherial fluids of the consciously "revisionist" disciples of John Hutchinson. The shifting political and theological currents of the 1780's, and more especially the 1790's, the association of Priestley's ideas with "materialism," and the pressures on chemical theory inherent in the dramatic technological advances of the period, have not yet received any sustained investigation. For instance, the resonances between Dalton's philosophical position on the nature and properties of matter and the teachings of the Hutchinsonians may be more easily noted than explained. It is one of the curiosities of historical exegesis that the intellectual and philosophical context and consequences of what was for a century the dominant scientific theory of matter—the chemical atomic theory—have been so little studied. The situation is better when we turn to the more limited questions of the chronology and logic of the experimental work which fed and helped to fashion Dalton's evolving theoretical concerns.

Besides his mathematical interests, Dalton was early involved in natural history, the compiling of meteorological records, and the construction of barometers, thermometers, rain gauges, and hygrometers. His daily weather records over a five-year period and those of his friends John Gough and Peter Crosthwaite were to form the basis of Dalton's first book. The *Meteorological Observations and Essays* (Manchester, 1793) well displays the interests, ambitions, and considerable energy of the young provincial natural philosopher. Already with the printer before he left Kendal, the work provides tables of barometric pressure, temperature, wind, humidity, and rainfall, besides detailing the occurrences of snow, thunder, and the aurora borealis. All these constitute the *Observations*. As such they testify to John's patience and diligence. Far more interesting are the *Essays* where the empirical is made the servant of the speculative.

The *Essays* include a theory of trade winds (anticipated by George Hadley, as Dalton discovered on his move to Manchester with its more adequate libraries), a theory of the aurora borealis (similarly anticipated by Anders Celsius and by Edmond Halley), speculations about variations in barometric pressure (this time anticipated by Jean De Luc), and ideas on evaporation which include the germs of his own later chemical atomic theory.[11]

Dalton's earliest meteorological researches had awakened a deep and abiding interest in the state of water vapor in the atmosphere, and the theory of rain. In the *Meteorological Observations* he advanced "a theory of the state of vapour in the atmosphere, which, as far as I can discover, is entirely new, and will be found, I believe, to solve all the phenomena of vapour we are acquainted with." The theory was that "evaporation and the condensation of vapour are not the effects of chemical affinities, but that aqueous vapour always exists as a fluid *sui generis,* diffused among the rest of the aerial fluids . . . there is no need to suppose a chemical attraction in the case." [12]

In denying the chemical attraction of water for air in which it was "dissolved," Dalton was flouting the orthodox and Newtonian view that short-range attractive and repulsive forces were the appropriate agents for explaining the process. With his habit of looking upon all empirical phenomena from a mathematical point of view, Dalton was not the one to worry about this. His experiments seemed to show that the absorbtion of water vapor by air *was not pressure dependent,* that is, "that a cubic foot of dry air, whatever its density be, will imbibe the same weight of vapour if the temperature be the same." Such a conclusion (in present-day terms "that the vapour pressure of water is constant at constant temperature") could not easily be reconciled with belief in evaporation as a chemical process. Dalton, the mathematically inclined meteorologist, simply abandoned the chemistry!

In fact he went even further, saying "that the vapour of water (and probably of most other liquids) exists at all times in the at-

11. For Dalton's meteorological activities, and the theorists who anticipated him, see Henry Lonsdale, *John Dalton,* The Worthies of Cumberland, no. 5 (1874), chs. 4 and 5; W. E. K. Middleton, *A History of the Theories of Rain* (Oldbourne, 1965), ch. 7; Sir Harold Hartley, "John Dalton, F.R.S. (1766–1844) and the Atomic Theory —A Lecture to Commemorate his Bicentenary," *Proceedings of the Royal Society,* series A, *300* (1967), 291–315.

12. Dalton, *Meteorology,* pp. vi and 132–136.

mosphere in an independent state." As the quotation shows, Dalton was not afraid to generalize his ideas. The visual nature of his thinking, and the essential continuity in his own ideas from before 1793 right down to 1808, is apparent from his supporting statements. Dalton argued that it was an error to assume chemical combination was necessary if water vapor was to exist in the open atmosphere below 212° F. The error arose from assuming "that air pressing upon vapour condenses the vapour equally with vapour pressing upon vapour, a supposition we have no right to assume, and which I apprehend will plainly appear to be contradictory to reason, and unwarranted by facts; for, *when a particle of vapour exists between two particles of air let their equal and opposite pressures upon it be what they may, they cannot bring it nearer to another particle of vapour.*" [13]

The ideas that in a mixture of gases every gas acts as an independent entity ("Dalton's law of partial pressures") and that the air is *not* a vast chemical solvent were first stated in the 1793 *Meteorological Observations*. The statements brought no immediate reaction. This was only to be expected. Dalton's arguments were at the time tentative and undeveloped, the ideas themselves curious in a world of all-pervasive chemical forces, and the author and vehicle of publication comparatively obscure.

Three papers that Dalton read to the Manchester Literary and Philosophical Society in 1799 and 1800 (in which year he became the Society's secretary) show how much the question of water vapor continued to exercise him. The first paper analyzed the balance in nature between rain, dew, river water runoff, and evaporation. In the course of his discussion Dalton provided the earliest definition of the dew point. Then followed two competent but more pedestrian papers on heat. In them his firm belief in a fluid of heat is well displayed, and his complete acceptance of the particular caloric theory of William Irvine and Adair Crawford is apparent.[14] The really dramatic development came in the summer of 1801.

13. *Ibid.,* pp. 200–202.
14. *Manchester Memoirs* 5 (1802), 346–372, and 515–526. See also the article by R. Fox in Cardwell, *Dalton and Science,* pp. 187–201.

FROM MIXED GASES TO CHEMICAL PHILOSOPHY

By 14 September 1801 Dalton was confident enough in his ideas to write to William Nicholson's recently established monthly *Journal of Natural Philosophy, Chemistry and the Arts.* This showed no hesitation in publishing Dalton's paper on a "New theory of the constitution of mixed aeriform fluids, and particularly of the atmosphere."

That Dalton was convinced of the value of his ideas is apparent. The rough sketch of his theory of mixed gases printed in Nicholson's *Journal,* was quickly supplemented in three papers to the Manchester society. These included the first clear statement that "when two elastic fluids, denoted by A and B, are mixed together, there is no mutual repulsion amongst their particles; that is, the particles of A do not repel those of B, as they do one another. Consequently, the pressure or whole weight upon any one particle arises solely from those of its own kind." [15] The debt of this generalized "new theory" to the 1793 picture of water vapor in air is obvious. So too is the debt of Dalton's thinking, with its static, particulate gas, to the passage in Newton's *Principia* (Book II, Proposition 23) which discussed the properties that such a gas would have. Besides this first formal enunciation of the law of gaseous partial pressures, the papers also contained important information on evaporation and on steam pressure, not to mention Dalton's independent statement of Charles's law that "all elastic fluids expand the same quantity by heat."

Dalton's 1793 statements had passed unnoticed. The reaction to his 1801 pronouncements was rapid and widespread. The three papers in the *Manchester Memoirs* were abstracted and reprinted throughout Europe. Discussion was immediate and lively. C. L.

15. *Manchester Memoirs* 5 (1802), 535–602. This series of essays presents the earliest example of (as also Dalton's first opportunity for) alteration before publication. The printed version seems to have incorporated material from a paper read in April 1800, as well as the three 1801 papers. This may be seen by comparing the titles of the papers when read (Lonsdale, *Dalton,* pp. 309–310) and when published. See also *Journal of Natural Philosophy, Chemistry and the Arts* (referred to below as *Nicholson's Journal*), [quarto series], 5 (1802), 241–244.

Berthollet—then in the midst of his Newtonian affinity investigations—scornfully dismissed Dalton's diagrammatic representation of the new theory of mixed gases as "un tableau d'imagination." Humphry Davy quickly sought the judgment of a friend on these "new and very singular" ideas. Even the Literary and Philosophical Society was uncertain what to make of its secretary's dismissal of chemical affinity as a force acting in the atmosphere. More damagingly, the 1802 first edition of Thomas Thomson's highly successful textbook, *A System of Chemistry,* was openly critical. Dalton quickly wrote to both the major monthly scientific journals of the day, rebutting Thomson's criticism.[16] Yet it was not argument that was needed so much as convincing experimental proof of his beliefs. To provide such proof became Dalton's major aim, and thus the efficient cause of the chemical atomic theory. What began as a particular interest in meteorology ended up as a powerful and wide-ranging new approach to the whole of chemistry, though the transition was by no means sudden.

In the course of 1802, between his heavy teaching commitments ("I have about eight or nine day pupils . . . and am now giving upwards of twenty lessons per week, privately . . . besides"),[17] Dalton was endeavoring both to further his researches on heat and to provide supporting evidence for his heavily attacked theory of mixed gases. With this latter end in view he began an experimental enquiry into the proportions of the various gases in the atmosphere. It was this enquiry which accidentally raised the whole question of the solubility of gases in water. As Dalton subsequently put it:

In 1802 . . . I was engaged in an investigation of the quantity of carbonic acid in the atmosphere; it was matter of surprise to me that lime

16. See C. L. Berthollet, *Essai de Statique Chimique* (Paris, 1803), I, 499; J. A. Paris, *The Life of Sir Humphry Davy* (1831), I, 157; *Nicholson's Journal 8* (1804), 297; T. Thomson, *A System of Chemistry* (Edinburgh, 1802), III, 270; *Philosophical Magazine 14* (1802), 169–173; *Nicholson's Journal 3* (1802), 267–271.

17. From a 22 March 1802 letter to Elihu Robinson, quoted in Lonsdale, *Dalton,* p. 153.

water should so readily manifest the presence of carbonic acid in the air, whilst pure water by exposure for any length of time, gave not the least traces of that acid. I thought that length of time ought to compensate for weakness of affinity. In pursuing the subject I found that the quantity of this acid taken up by water was greater or less in proportion to its greater or less density in the gaseous mixture, incumbent upon the surface, and therefore ceased to be surprised at water absorbing so insensible a portion from the atmosphere.

The accuracy of this statement is supported by Dalton's own "Index of Notes" and by Roscoe and Harden's inventory of his notebooks. The latter shows that "the last four months of this year [1802] were occupied with experiments on lime water, on the carbonic acid in air . . . and on the solubility of carbonic acid, air, and other gases in water." [18]

By 12 November Dalton had discovered enough to read to the "Lit and Phil" a paper "On the Proportion of the several Gases or Elastic Fluids, constituting the Atmosphere; with an Enquiry into the Circumstances which distinguish the *Chemical* and *Mechanical* Absorption of Gases by Liquids." When read, though not when published, the paper contained a statement to the effect that " [carbonic acid] gas is held in water, not by chemical affinity, but merely by the pressure of the gas . . . on the surface, forcing it into the pores of the water." [19] Dalton's accidently begun researches on solubility thus led to an extension of his mechanical ideas.

William Henry was among those hostile to the mixed gases theory. When (presumably before the lecture on the subject) Dalton informed his friend of the extension of the theory to explain gas-liquid interactions, it seems that Henry was provoked to begin

18. See J. Dalton, *A New System of Chemical Philosophy*, pt. 1 (1808), pp. 182–183; H. E. Roscoe and A. Harden, *A New View of the Origin of Dalton's Atomic Theory* (1896), p. 55. The "Index of Notes" is in the possession of the Manchester Literary and Philosophical Society. Under "Absorption of gases by water" (one of its few headings) there are frequent entries for 1801 and 1803.

19. Lonsdale, *Dalton*, p. 310; *Nicholson's Journal* 3 (1802), 271, quoting a letter written by Dalton six days after reading the paper.

his own "extensive series of experiments, with a view to ascertain the order of affinities of gases for water." These were not a success. However by 8 December 1802, Henry had found what Dalton failed to see, namely "the following general law: *that, under equal circumstances of temperature, water takes up, in all cases, the same volume of condensed gas as of gas under ordinary pressure.*" Although Dalton had missed what became "Henry's Law," he was clearly aware of Henry's work. He was also quick to see its relevance to his own ideas, and to convince Henry of that relevance. As he later recorded in a quietly triumphant way

I had not however entertained any suspicion that this law was generally applicable to the gases till Dr Henry's discovery was announced. Immediately upon this, it struck me as essentially necessary in ascertaining the quantity of any gas which a given volume of water will absorb, that we must be careful the gas is perfectly pure or unmixed with any other gas whatever; otherwise the maximum effect for any given pressure cannot be produced. This thought was suggested to Dr Henry, and found to be correct; in consequence of which, it became expedient to repeat some of his experiments relating to the quantity of gas absorbed under a given pressure. Upon due consideration of all these phenomena, Dr Henry became convinced, that there was no system of elastic fluids which gave so simple, easy and intelligible a solution of them, as the one I adopt, namely, that each gas in any mixture exercises a distinct pressure, which continues the same if the other gases are withdrawn.

The accuracy of this account is confirmed by Henry's writings. His later admission that his "experiments . . . were made under impressions very unfavourable to . . . [Dalton's] hypothesis" is in keeping with the way in which his December report, announcing Henry's Law, still showed evidence of a chemical affinity approach to gas-solubility problems. Yet by March 1803 he was admitting that some of his experimental results were "rather below the truth" and that "the theory which Mr Dalton has suggested to me on this subject, and which appears to be confirmed by my experiments, is, that the absorption of gases by water is purely a mechanical effect."[20] What began as an attempt to refute Dalton's mechanical ideas ended up as an impressive confirmation of them.

In Dalton's notebooks for 1803 "January, February and March were chiefly occupied with work on the solubility of gases in water." The importance he attached to these studies is clearly shown in a March letter to his brother saying "I have been, as usual, fully engaged in all my leisure hours, in the pursuit of chemical and philosophical enquiries. Even my Christmas vacation was taken up in this way; indeed I have had considerable success of late in this line, having got into a *track that has not been much trod in before.*"[21] However, in April Dalton appears to have left the gas solubility studies which had occupied so much time and returned to his researches on heat.

As Roscoe and Harden record, "The remainder of the month of April, and the whole of May and June were devoted to researches on the phenomena of heat, expansion of liquids, expansion of water in different vessels, force of steam, etc." The return to heat studies may well have been encouraged by the receipt of the April *Nicholson's Journal*. This contained a letter referring to Dalton's work on the real zero of heat, to which he duly replied.[22] In July the usual annual holiday in the Lake District took place and, somewhat more unusually, a visit to London. While in London Dalton, now a man of rising scientific reputation, investigated the prospect of arranging some lectures at the Royal Institution. On his return he wrote to his brother that "I have not heard from the manager of the Royal Institution yet since I left London; am therefore undetermined on that head." It was in fact on 18 July that the Committee of Science of that body proposed that he be engaged in the ensuing session.[23] The series of lectures duly took place in December and January.

20. *Philosophical Transactions of the Royal Society 93* (1803), 41; Dalton, *New System*, p. 183; *Philosophical Transactions of the Royal Society 93* (1803), 274–276.

21. Roscoe and Harden, *New View*, p. 55; the 21 March 1803 letter to Jonathan Dalton is quoted in Henry, *Memoirs of Dalton*, p. 47.

22. *Nicholson's Journal 4* (1803), 220–224, and 5 (1803), 34–36.

23. See the 1803 letter to Jonathan Dalton quoted in *Manchester Memoirs 59* (1914–1915), no. 12, p. 4; B. Jones, *The Royal Institution* (1871), p. 216.

Back at work in Manchester in August, Dalton reverted to the studies of gaseous solubility which he had left in April. He also found time to write a note to *Nicholson's Journal* on 22 August, defending his theory of mixed gases against the rival chemical affinity explanation. Though gas solubility phenomena had provided Dalton with unexpected but welcome confirmation of his mechanical ideas, he was obviously aware of the weaknesses still present in his theory. As he recorded in a paper read to the "Lit and Phil" on October 21, "The greatest difficulty attending the mechanical hypothesis [of gas-water solubility], arises from different gases observing different laws. Why does water not admit its bulk of every kind of gas alike?" It was to this same paper that the first public list of particle weights was appended, for as Dalton went on to say

This question I have duly considered, and though I am not yet able to satisfy myself completely, I am nearly persuaded that the circumstance depends upon the weight and number of the ultimate particles of the several gases: Those whose particles are lightest and single being least absorbable and the others more according as they increase in weight and complexity. An enquiry into the relative weights of the ultimate particles of bodies is a subject, as far as I know, entirely new: I have lately been prosecuting this enquiry with remarkable success. The principle cannot be entered upon in this paper; but I shall just subjoin the results, as far as they appear to be ascertained by my experiments.[24]

It thus seems clear that Dalton's crucial decision to investigate "the relative weights of the ultimate particles of bodies" arose from his continuing endeavor to find wider experimental support for his theory of mixed gases. The revolutionary nature of what he chose to do at this juncture lay not in the realm of concepts or methodology but rather in the question he selected for investigation. As Dalton himself expressed it, it was the *enquiry* into the relative weights of the ultimate particles of bodies that was entirely new. That enquiry of course demanded its own guide lines

24. *Nicholson's Journal 6* (1803), 118–120; *Manchester Memoirs 6* (1805), 286.

and assumptions, and it was here that the theory of mixed gases controlled as well as caused the whole investigation.

In accord with the postulates of this theory Dalton assumed that when two elements A and B come together in reaction, it is the mutual repulsion of the atoms of B that is the critical factor in determining what happens, rather than any attraction between A and B. Assuming spherical atoms of equal size, twelve atoms of B can theoretically come into contact (react) with one of A. In practice the most likely outcome is a one-to-one combination of A and B. Two atoms of B combining with one of A is also possible, but less likely as the atoms of B have a mutual repulsion to overcome, even though they will automatically take up positions on opposite sides of A. Three atoms of B to one of A means greater repulsive forces, and a corresponding triangular disposition, and so on. Thus if only one chemical compound of elements A and B is known, it is natural to assume it has the composition AB. If there are two compounds, they are most likely to be AB and AB_2, and so on.[25] In this way Dalton's theoretical views provided a rationale for deciding both the formulae of compounds and their three-dimensional molecular structures. Armed with such a mechanical view of combining ratios and the calculating system it implied, it was a simple matter for him to argue from the knowledge that eight ounces of oxygen combine with one of hydrogen, to the statement that the relative weights of their ultimate particles are as eight to one.

The September 1803 particle weights theory arrived at in this way had only moderate success in resolving "the greatest difficulty of the mechanical hypothesis" of solubility. Its use for that purpose was subsequently abandoned. The rules of combination proved more fascinating and chemically illuminating. Already by September Dalton had elucidated a scheme relating the nitrogen oxides to one another. In his usual quietly accurate way he later recorded how "so far back as the year 1803 I had resolved in my

25. Dalton publicly set out this rationale in his "Observations on Dr. Bostock's Review of the Atomic Principles of Chemistry," *Nicholson's Journal* 29 (1811), 143–151.

mind the various combinations then known of azote and oxygen, and had determined almost without doubts, that nitrous gas [in modern terminology, NO, nitric oxide] is a binary compound and nitrous oxide [N_2O, nitrous oxide] a ternary." In October he again succeeded (as he had first, early in August) in obtaining experimental results agreeable to his newly elaborated ideas about the possible reactions of nitric oxide and oxygen. By varying the reaction conditions, Dalton found he could make oxygen combine with 1.7 (in August; 1.8, in October) or 3.4 (in August; 3.6, in October) times its volume of nitric oxide (NO, nitrous gas to him). This result has proved difficult for subsequent experimenters to duplicate. In any case Dalton does not appear to have attached very great importance to it, though it did apparently show combination taking place in accord with his rules.[26] Instead, he began work on the combining proportions of common hydrocarbons, in the hope of finding more straightforward illustrations of his theoretical ideas. In the choice of these gases, the influence of William Henry may be seen once again. From his earliest paper to the Royal Society onwards, Henry had made the hydrocarbons his special interest. These new chemical investigations were not, however, of such overwhelming importance as to make Dalton neglect his heat studies, on which he read a further paper to the "Lit and Phil" late in the year.

In the midst of all these activities an ominous cloud had appeared on the horizon. It took the form of a paper by John Gough, Dalton's erstwhile tutor, sharply challenging the mixed gases theory. This paper, "An Essay on the Theory of Mixed Gases, and the State of Water in the Atmosphere," was duly read to the Manchester Society on 4 November. Together with the reply Dalton wrote privately to Gough, it was to touch off a con-

26. See Roscoe and Harden, *New View*, pp. 35 and 59–60; Nash, "Origin of Atomic Theory," pp. 104–105; Partington, *History*, III, 790–791. As was shown in ch. 3 above, A. N. Meldrum made this work on the oxides of nitrogen the center of his account of Dalton's "discovery" of the atomic theory. Nash and Partington discuss the difficulties in trying to reproduce Dalton's results, which are presumably based on the reactions $2NO+O_2+H_2O \rightarrow HNO_2+HNO_3$ and $4NO+O_2+2H_2O \rightarrow 4HNO_2$.

troversy lasting almost two years.[27] With affairs in this state—a new theory of the combinations of bodies apparently supported by the nitrogen oxides, though not as yet by the hydrocarbons; a list of particle weights not fully supporting an idea about gas solubilities, though the actual solubility phenomena reinforced a theory of mixed gases; the mixed gases theory itself the subject of fresh controversy and attack—Dalton set off for London to give his Royal Institution lectures.

With his customary scrupulous concern for historical accuracy, Dalton in 1808 was to say that "a brief outline of [the primary laws of heat and chemical combination] was first publicly given . . . in a course of lectures on natural philosophy, at the Royal Institution in London." It would be rewarding to know in detail the elements of this "brief outline." That is unfortunately not possible. However, some facts survive. Dalton's notebook entry for 22 December 1803 (the first day of the lectures) shows that he lost no time in discussing the nitrogen oxides with Davy, an acknowledged authority on those gases. In view of Davy's familiarity with the technical problems, it must have been all the more disappointing to Dalton that his ideas signally failed to impress the London virtuoso. Many years later he was bitterly to record how "from the observations of Sir Humphry, however, the speculation appeared to him rather more ingenious than important." [28]

Davy was not the only one to be treated to Dalton's arguments. At least one public auditor was more perceptive, though still seeing the rules for determining combining ratios as the essence of Dalton's ideas. In a discussion of Berthollet's vastly different views on chemical combination, in the *Literary Journal* for November 1804, an anonymous reviewer chose to say that "Mr Dal-

27. See *Manchester Memoirs* 6 (1805), 296–316, 425–436; *Nicholson's Journal 9* (1804), 52–57, 89–92 ff. The Mss. of nine long letters that passed between Gough and Luke Howard, continuing the controversy, are in the family archives of Thomas and Dorothy Hodgkin. The letters run from March through July 1805 and show that Dalton's theory of mixed gases was still provoking lively controversy among an intimate group of Quaker meteorologists, some four years after its initial formulation.

28. Dalton, *New System*, p. v; Roscoe and Harden, *New View*, pp. 43–44; see also ch. 6 below.

ton seems to be of opinion that bodies always combine in the same degree of intimacy, if they combine at all, and that the nature of the combination varies only when the proportions of the constituents vary. The very curious theory of *atoms,* which this philosopher explained last winter in his lectures in the Royal Institution, seems indeed, to lead irresistibly to this conclusion. Into this theory we do not at present enter; nor, indeed, would it be decorous to do so, as Mr Dalton has not yet thought proper to give it to the world." [29]

These various indications show that Dalton broached his ideas on chemical combination and at least mentioned a "very curious theory of atoms" before his London audience. However the public record and his extant letters all suggest that he concentrated heavily on his theories of heat and mixed gases in his lectures and private arguments. The largely untried ideas about chemical combination were still ones of uncertain worth, to be broached with caution.

The last lecture of the Royal Institution course was given on 25 January 1804, and by 1 February Dalton was in Manchester again. In his absence a further paper of Gough's criticizing the mixed gases theory had been read to the "Lit and Phil." Late in February Dalton wrote "my lately published essays on gases, etc., together with the more recent ones read at our Society, and of which I gave the result in my late lectures, have drawn the attention of most of the philosophers of Europe. They are busy with them at London, Edinburgh, Paris, and in various parts of Germany, some maintaining one side and some another. The truth will surely out at last." [30] This letter makes it clear that the controversy over mixed gases was central to Dalton's thinking at this time. Smyth's *Bibliography* amply confirms that Dalton's "lately published essays on gases, etc.," were indeed being actively considered on the Continent. Even so his researches continued to range over a wide field—diffusion, solubility, nitrous gas-oxygen

29. *Literary Journal 4* (1804), 515–516. I am indebted to Mr. J. B. Morrell for this reference.
30. Henry, *Memoirs of Dalton,* p. 50.

reactions, and the temperature of maximum density of water, as well as the extension of his rules of combination to the different classes of metal oxide.

In the spring of 1804, the second edition of Thomson's *System of Chemistry* was published. Though referring to Dalton himself in glowing terms, Thomson once again attacked the mixed gases theory. Dalton was quick to reply, writing off to both *Nicholson's Journal* and the *Philosophical Magazine*. This time he also took the added precaution of arranging for William Henry, his most influential—and perhaps his only—supporter, to read a paper in his defense at the "Lit and Phil" and to send copies of it to the two journals.[31] Thomas Thomson was quick to visit Henry, his old acquaintance, while on an August journey from Edinburgh to the south.

Early that same month Dalton, freshly back from his annual Lake District holiday, read a paper "On the Elements of Chemical Philosophy" to the "Lit and Phil."[32] The title reflected his newer interests. On the experimental front the whole of August was occupied with a fresh attack on the hydrocarbons. The attack finally succeeded in bringing these gases into line with his rules of combination on Friday, 24 August, 1804. Thus when Thomson and Dalton finally met over tea at William Henry's on Sunday, 26 August, they must have discussed mixed gases at length, but not surprisingly Dalton's ideas on chemical combination and the successful results of his recent experiments also entered the conversation. Years later, when mixed gases were forgotten but the "atomic theory" famous, Thomson not unnaturally only recalled this latter part of their conversation.[33]

It was around this period that Dalton's first calculations of the

31. *A System of Chemistry*, 2nd ed. (Edinburgh, 1804), III, 314–317; *Nicholson's Journal 8* (1804), 145–149 and 297–301; *Philosophical Magazine 19* (1804), 79–83 and 193–196.

32. Lonsdale, *Dalton*, p. 310. For reasons explained by Meldrum [*Manchester Memoirs 55* (1910–1911), no. 5, p. 12], Lonsdale, like R. A. Smith before him, misdated this paper. It was probably read on 17 August 1804.

33. Thomas Thomson, *A History of Chemistry* (1831), II, 289–292. Part of Thomson's account is reproduced in ch. 3 above. Its reliability is more fully examined in Thackray, "Daltonian Doubts Resolved," pp. 43, 55.

particle weights of alkalis appeared, and some further calculations on the metals were also undertaken. But the meeting with Thomson does not appear to have particularly influenced the tenor of his work. In the autumn his attention was again directed to experiments of various sorts on heat, two papers on the subject being read to the "Lit and Phil." Otherwise the continuing controversy with Gough seems to have been the main diversion.

Early in 1805, Dalton set off to London once more, to purchase apparatus for the course of lectures which he had decided to give in Manchester in the spring. The printed syllabus of the lectures has recently come to light. Though "similar to the one . . . [lately delivered] in the Royal Institution at London," [34] the Manchester course contains significant differences. By now a whole lecture was devoted to "the Elements of Bodies and their Composition," the inclusion of "reasons for the assumption of 1 to 1 combination" reflecting the basis of the combining rules in the theory of mixed gases. The combining rules were still applied only to gaseous substances, which shows the caution in Dalton's public thinking on the subject. Conversely, the prominent position given to the various carbon compounds shows how highly Dalton regarded his own elucidation of their relationships: thus

Carbon or charcoal and its combination
One charcoal and one oxygen—carbonic oxide
One charcoal and two oxygen—carbonic acid
One charcoal and one hydrogen—olefiant gas
One charcoal and two hydrogen—carburetted hydrogen from
    stagnant water, etc., etc.[35]

Though the absorption of gases by water was included and occupied a full lecture, the outline, unlike Dalton's 1803 paper, made no direct reference to particle weights. In all these ways it contrasts strongly with the new syllabus issued just two years later for his Edinburgh lectures. It was to be during these two years that Dalton's ideas about combining rules and particle weights were

34. As Dalton claimed in a 2 January 1805 prospectus, reproduced in Roscoe and Harden, *New View*, pp. 66–67.
35. Quoted from the syllabus, which is printed in full in ch. 6 below.

first provided with a new focus, then gradually organized in such a way that they could stand in their own right.

The first theory of mixed gases explained the equilibrium of the atmosphere and the sort of solubility phenomena investigated with the help of William Henry. The theory also had a less satisfactory side. As Dalton later admitted "this hypothesis, however beautiful might be its application, had some improbable features. We were to suppose as many distinct *kinds* of repulsive powers, as of gases; and, moreover, to suppose that *heat* was not the repulsive power in any one case; positions certainly not very probable." [36] In 1805 Dalton succeeded in eliminating these awkward features, by finding a mechanism which depended only on heat.

That ultimate particles of different chemicals differed in size was a direct consequence of Dalton's initial ideas. In 1803 he had explored this difference in connection with his particle-weight water-solubility studies. On 14 September 1805 he drew up for the second time a table of diameters of elastic particles, but this time the diameters were compared not with that of a water particle, as in 1803, but with hydrogen. As the later public account said "if the *sizes* be different, then on the supposition that the repulsive power is heat, no equilibrium can be established by particles of unequal sizes pressing against each other. This idea occurred to me in 1805. I soon found that the *sizes* of the particles of elastic fluids *must* be different." This "second theory of mixed gases" quickly established itself in Dalton's eyes, and in the 1808 *New System* he could say "my present views on the subject of mixed gases . . . are somewhat different from what they were when the theory was announced." These present views were those of the second theory, namely *"that every species of pure elastic fluid has its particles globular and all of a size; but that no two species agree in the size of their particles . . .* [and that] the phenomena of mixed gases may still be accounted for, by repulsion,

36. Roscoe and Harden, *New View*, pp. 16–17. The quotation comes from Dalton's 1810–1811 lectures at the Royal Institution.

without the postulatum, that their particles are mutually inelastic." [37]

The second theory was not without its own difficulties. For instance, the size variation between particles of different chemicals was by no means as large as might have been wished. Perhaps in recognition of such problems, and in marked contrast to his earlier attitude, Dalton never publicized the second theory with any vigor. Nevertheless, it did provide a fresh impetus to his weight studies for "it became an object to determine the relative sizes and weights [of the particles of elastic fluids] . . . Other bodies besides elastic fluids, namely liquids and solids, were subject to investigation, in consequence of their combining with elastic fluids. Thus a train of investigation was laid for determining the *number* and *weight* of all chemical elementary principles which enter into any sort of combination one with another." [38]

Dalton in this statement considerably simplified a complex development, ignoring his earlier unsuccessful work in connection with gas solubilities and his tentative consideration of the metals. His action is understandable. The difficulty about particle weights is neither belief in their existence nor the obtaining of the data from which they may be measured; the work of William Higgins and Dalton's own 1803 studies both show this. The difficulty is that without a fully articulated theory of definite and multiple proportions, and a whole complex of information on reacting quantities, *particle weight studies lack chemical utility.* Indeed the need for this complex of information was soon to become painfully obvious to Thomas Thomson, J. J. Berzelius, and those other chemists who rightly saw in Dalton's work a new quantitative basis for chemistry. In this light it is understandable how detection of but a few confirming instances of multiple proportions should seem so important to Dalton, and particle weights of but little interest at first, unless supporting a solubility theory or helping to establish a new mixed gases hypothesis.

37. Roscoe and Harden, *New View*, pp. 16–17, 41, 65; Dalton, *New System*, p. 188–189. See also Thackray, "Daltonian Doubts Resolved," p. 45.
38. Roscoe and Harden, *New View*, p. 17.

Not a great deal is known about Dalton's activities in the later part of 1805 and through 1806. In November 1805 he wrote to his brother that "I contemplate a repetition of my lectures during the winter, and am preparing a work of my own for the press"— presumably the *New System,* to which this is the first known reference. Otherwise Dalton seems to have been largely occupied with further experiments on heat. He read a paper "On Respiration and Animal Heat" to the "Lit and Phil" on 7 March. On 14 April he wrote to *Nicholson's Journal* about the contraction of water by heat. And, to quote Roscoe and Harden, "the whole of April and May and the greater part of June, was entirely occupied (the notes extend to about fifty pages) with experiments and speculations on heat, the final results of which are embodied in the *New System,* part I." [39] As the notebook entries make clear, "experiments and speculations on heat" were by now intimately associated with ideas about the gaseous state, the relative sizes of atoms, and so on.

In the late summer and autumn Dalton was busy revising and extending his particle weight studies to include metals and salts, though on 30 November 1806 he wrote giving a glimpse of the other side of his life in a letter of familiar sound: "I am very busy, being in the midst of a course of lectures, and having a good deal of private tuition besides." [40] The following February Dalton read a paper to the "Lit and Phil" on "The Constitution and Properties of Sulphuric Acid." The title indicates the sort of chemical enquiry now occupying his attention. Finally in March he set off to Edinburgh. There he delivered the course of lectures in which his "new system of chemical philosophy" was first clearly set forth for public consideration. His introduction is so typical of Dalton and so well illustrates the manner in which his thoughts had progressed, as well as the hopes he now entertained for his ideas, that it deserves quotation:

39. See the 10 November 1805 letter to Jonathan Dalton, quoted in Henry, *Memoirs of Dalton,* p. 64; Lonsdale, *Dalton,* p. 311; *Nicholson's Journal 13* (1806), 377–380; Roscoe and Harden, *New View,* p. 71.

40. Roscoe and Harden, *New View,* p. 74; letter to Jonathan Dalton, *Manchester Memoirs 59* (1914–1915), no. 12, p. 8.

It may appear somewhat like presumption in a stranger to intrude himself upon your notice in the character I am now assuming, in a city like this, so deservedly famous for its seminaries of physical science. My apology, however, shall be brief. The field of science is large; it is, therefore, impossible for any individual to cultivate the whole. My attention has been directed for several years past, with considerable assiduity, to the subjects of *heat,* of *elastic fluids,* of the *primary elements* of bodies, and the *mode of their combinations.* In the prosecution of these studies several new and important facts and observations have occurred. I have been enabled to reduce a number of apparently anomalous facts to general laws, and to exhibit a new view of the first principles or elements of bodies and their combinations, which, if established, as I doubt not it will in time, will produce the most important changes in the system of chemistry, and reduce the whole to a science of great simplicity, and intelligible to the meanest understanding. My object in the proposed short course of lectures is to exhibit to you the grounds and reasoning on which I entertain those ideas. I chose Edinburgh and Glasgow in preference to any other cities in Britain because I apprehend the doctrines inculcated would in those cities meet with the most rigid scrutiny, which is what I desire. This is my only apology.[41]

Dalton's course, given twice in Edinburgh and once in Glasgow, consisted of two lectures on heat and three on the chemical elements. The printed syllabus (see Chapter 6 and Figure 5) shows how in these lectures he set forth the results of his own researches, expounding his ideas on heat and chemical combination. His arguments covered such topics as "Elastic Fluids conceived to consist of indivisible particles or atoms of matter, surrounded with atmospheres of Heat," "Reasons for believing that in the Chemical Union of Elementary Principles, we shall generally, if not always, find a compound consisting of 1 atom of each," and "Coincidences of these [combinations] with experimental results." The fully fledged nature of his ideas is shown by the inclusion of "Weights of the ultimate particles of Acids, Alkalis, Earths, and Metals." Going even further, he anticipated the subsequent experimental findings of Thomson and W. H. Wollaston

41. The introduction is printed in Roscoe, *Dalton and Modern Chemistry,* pp. 166–167.

LECT. III. IV. & V.

Of Chemical Elements.

Elastic Fluids conceived to consist of indivisible particles or atoms of matter, surrounded with atmospheres of Heat.—Liquid and solid bodies conceived likewise to be composed of atoms surrounded with Heat, but in a state of much greater proximity, by virtue of the attraction of aggregation.—Reasons for believing, that in the Chemical Union of Elementary Principles, we shall generally, if not always, find a compound, consisting of 1 atom of each.—That the next most simple combination is 1 atom with 2.—That such combinations always take place before more complex ones, which in reality do rarely occur. Water, 1 atom of oxygen and 1 of hydrogen; Ammoniac, 1 atom of azot and 1 of hydrogen; Nitrous Gas, 1 atom of azot and 1 of oxygen; Nitric Acid, 1 azot and 2 oxygen; Nitrous Oxide, 1 azot and 2 oxygen, &c. coincidences of these with experimental results. Carbonic Oxide, 1 charcoal and 1 oxygen; Carbonic Acid, 1 charcoal and 2 oxygen; Olefient Gas, 1 charcoal and 1 hydrogen; Carburetted Hydrogen, 1 charcoal and 2 hydrogen,

5. Part of an 1807 Lecture Syllabus. Prepared for Dalton's Edinburgh audience. (Courtesy of the Manchester Literary and Philosophical Society.)

by arguing that "Carbonates, etc. are 1 carbonic acid and 1 base; Subcarbonates etc. are 1 acid and 2 base; Supercarbonates etc. are 2 acid and 1 base, etc."

By March 1807 Dalton's chemical ideas had reached fruition, in marked contrast to the position only two years earlier. The lectures in Scotland were little short of a manifesto for the *New System*. That their reception was favorable we know from the dedication attached to the first part of that work when it finally appeared, just over a year later. With the publication of the second part of the *New System* in 1810, and more especially with Thomas Thomson's and W. H. Wollaston's 1808 papers showing the practical power of his approach, the chemical atomic theory was finally launched.[42] The theory was Dalton's last creative piece of scientific thinking, though he continued active work in several fields for more than a quarter-century subsequently. The main thrust of much of this work was in providing experimental measurements of atomic weights of known chemical compounds. The enormity of this task, and Dalton's reluctance to take other people's results on trust, are symbolized by his failure ever to complete those later parts of the *New System* which were to embody his results (though "Volume 2, Part 1" did belatedly appear in 1827).[43]

If the task of measuring atomic weights was to provide practical employment throughout the nineteenth century, Dalton's equation of the words atom and chemical element was likewise to be at the center of theoretical debate. Dalton's theory provided a new, fundamental, and enormously fruitful model of reality for the chemist. As such it gave focus and rationale to those weight studies that had become of steadily increasing importance to the

42. The two papers, published together and both explicitly referring to Dalton's ideas, were T. Thomson, "On Oxalic Acid," *Philosophical Transactions of the Royal Society of London* 98 (1808), 63–95; and W. H. Wollaston "On Super-Acid and Sub-Acid Salts," *ibid.*, pp. 96–102.

43. W. Henry was to write in 1820 that "Mr. Dalton proceeds slowly in printing another volume of his *System*, having, as he goes on, to work out the facts which are to support his general reasonings. His last subject of experiments was that of metallic alloys . . ." W. Henry to S. Hibbert-Ware, 26 March 1820. John Rylands Library. Eng. Mss. 994 f. 103.

science through the previous two generations. Even so, the systematic utilization and extension of his work on atomic weights was to be plagued by methodological problems—problems only slowly resolved through the investigations of J. L. Gay-Lussac, A. Avogadro, and S. Cannizzaro. Dalton's ideas on the real physical existence and actual nature of chemical *atoms* were to prove even more troublesome. They initiated a continuing nineteenth century debate that was terminated only by the work of Rutherford and Soddy. The background to that debate may be followed elsewhere.[44] Here it is sufficient to note that, whatever the historical and historiographical problems which still surround Dalton's ideas, the actual emergence of chemical atomic theory from his prior concerns with meteorology and mixed gases can now be understood.

44. Thackray, *Atoms and Powers*, esp. sec. 8.6.1; and D. M. Knight, *Atoms and Elements* (1967).

6. Documents on Chemical Atomic Theory

*It is the obvious duty of a
conscientious historian to record
faithfully all documents in his
possession.*
                        W. C. Henry in 1854

Despite the ravages of time and war, it is still possible to establish many fresh and important facts concerning the origins of Dalton's chemical atomic theory. Supposedly conscientious historians of the Victorian era were more often than not disarmingly casual in their search for and use of documentary evidence. Much carefully preserved and easily accessible material on Dalton's early years was left neglected and unexamined. Even documents crucial to an understanding of the origins of chemical atomic theory were lightly passed over. The historian of science cannot afford such a relaxed tolerance. Despite the tragic destruction of the major archive of Dalton manuscript in 1940, a careful gleaning of the field proves surprisingly rewarding, throwing new light on a variety of important issues.

THE 1803 PARTICLE WEIGHT MEASUREMENTS

It is now well established that Dalton made his first measurements of "the relative weights of ultimate particles" in September 1803. Historians have been somewhat embarrassed by the lack of any known public statement by Dalton himself which unequivocally attributes this development to the year 1803.[1] It is therefore

1. The 1808 preface to Dalton's *New System of Chemical Philosophy* does say that "in 1803, he [Dalton] was gradually led to those primary laws which seem to obtain in regard to heat, and to chemical combinations." Particle weights are not directly mentioned.

of interest to discover that in a talk Dalton gave to the "Lit and Phil" in October 1830, he specifically referred to his 1803 measurements. The badly war-damaged manuscript of Dalton's talk, which is reproduced in full below, is particularly significant. It (a) provides a clear statement by Dalton about the particle weight measurements of September 1803; (b) shows how Dalton was rebuffed when he explained his ideas to Davy at the end of that year; (c) indicates that Dalton was well informed on the controversy over his ideas in the 1820's; (d) reveals that he was well able to defend his own atomic symbols; and (e) provides the only known discussion of J. B. Richter's work [2] by Dalton. Unfortunately the manuscript is badly charred and at least one-third destroyed (see Figure 6). The dotted spaces in the reproduction represent the approximate length of breaks in the manuscript, and the material in square brackets, my conjectural reconstruction of an occasional small break.

CHEMICAL OBSERVATIONS ON CERTAIN ATOMIC WEIGHTS AS ADOPTED
BY DIFFERENT AUTHORS, WITH REMARKS ON THE NOTATION
OF BERZELIUS

Read 1830, October 15.

A series of essays read before this Society and afterwards published in the 5th volume of their *Memoirs* [3] gradually led me to the consideration of ultimate particles or atoms and of their combinations. Under the date of Sept. 3rd, 1803, I find in my notebook "Observations on the ultimate particles of bodies and their combinations," in which the atomic symbols which I still use [were] introduced. On the 23rd of October the same year [I r]ead my essay of the absorption of gases by [water] at the conclusion of which a series of atomic [weights] was given for

2. The possibility that J. B. Richter's work on chemical equivalents was a major source for Dalton's ideas is explored in H. E. Guerlac, "Some Daltonian Doubts," *Isis* 52 (1961), 544–554; and A. Thackray, "Daltonian Doubts Resolved," *Isis* 57 (1966), 35–55. See also ch. 3 above.

3. *Manchester Memoirs* 5 (1802), 535–602.

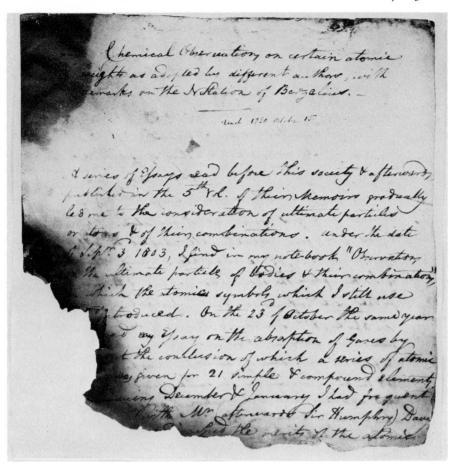

6. The Manuscript of Dalton's 1830 Lecture. Deposited in the archives of the Manchester Literary and Philosophical Society and damaged by fire in 1940. (Courtesy of the Society.)

21 simple and compound elements.[4] [In the en]suing December and January I had frequent [conversations] with Mr (afterwards Sir Humphry) Davy [in which we] discussed the merits of the atomic . . .

[Bottom of page burnt away]

4. See H. E. Roscoe and A. Harden, *A New View of the Origin of Dalton's Atomic Theory* (1896), p. 26; *Manchester Memoirs* 6 (1805), 271. Dalton appears to be two or three days out in both his dates.

[*page* 2]

nitrous oxide, nitrous gas and nitric (nitrous) acid, which Sir Humphry had so ably investigated in his researches then recently published.[5] I was the more happy in this as his results formed some of the most excellent exemplifications of the principles. The *heavy* nitrous oxide consisting of two atoms of azote and one of oxygen, the *light* nitrous gas consisting of one atom azote and one of oxygen, and the *heavy* nitrous acid gas, consisting of one atom of azote and two of oxygen, seemed well adapted to afford an illustration of the principles. From the observations of Sir Humphry however the speculation appeared to him rather more ingenious than important.

In April 1807 I delivered a series of lectures [largely] on atomic principles in Edinburgh and Glasgow . . . . . . The first part of *System of Chemistry* was published [in 1808]. At the end of December the same year Gay [-Lussac] read a paper, on the combination of gaseous [volumes] which was published in the 2nd volume of the [*Memoirs of*] *the Society d'Arcueil* in . . .[6]

[Bottom of page burnt away]

[*page* 3]

Dr Thomson was first acquainted with my views in 1806 [altered to 1804]. He gave some account of them in his *Chemistry* (3rd edit.) 1807.[7] He readily attached importance to them, and has ever since been occasionally engaged in the object of improving and extending them. In the series of *Annals of Philosophy* he has given several essays on the weights of atoms. He has changed some of the weights and modified others. Many of these alterations may be improvements, but his system of

5. Dalton talked with Davy while lodging at the Royal Institution for the duration of his lecture course. See ch. 5 above. Davy's own researches during this period may best be followed in J. Z. Fullmer, *Sir Humphry Davy's Published Works* (Cambridge, Mass., Harvard University Press, 1969).

6. On Gay-Lussac's work, see M. P. Crosland, *The Society of Arcueil* (Heinemann, 1967), pp. 354–360.

7. The meeting between Thomson and Dalton in 1804 is described in T. Thomson, *A History of Chemistry* (1831), II, 289. His 1807 account of Dalton's views is in his *A System of Chemistry*, 3rd ed. (Edinburgh, 1807), III, 424.

atoms, as it now stands, does not appear to me to be fixed upon a stable foundation.[8]

Sir H. Davy published a volume of *Chemistry* in 1812. His atomic numbers have much the same ratio as mine published in 1810, but they are all double of mine, owing to his adhering to the system of volumes, and taking 2 volumes of hydrogen for his standard of comparison and 1 volume of oxygen.

It is a remarkable fact that Dr Wollaston in publishing his logarithmic scale of chemical equivalents in 1814, should have [had] his object different from an investigation of the relative [weights] of atoms. The fact was inconsistent with his general [approach]. Dr Wollaston's Paper was read at the Royal [Society] in Nov. 1813.[9]

Berzelius, since 1811, has been continually engaged [in pu]blishing a system of atoms, chemical equiva[lents or] definite proportions, and what is of more im[portance has] been assiduous in endeavouring to . . .

[Bottom of page burnt away]

[*page 4*]

to form the several compounds. As for his system of combinations, it is very perplexing on account of its being founded on that of volumes, in accordance with Davy's, and yet having a special regard to atoms.

Berzelius' first atomic table may be seen in the *Annals of Philosophy* for May 1814. Oxygen gas is made the standard and is denoted by 100. Other bodies are supposed to be reduced to the form of gas and their weights in that state entered in the table, the weight of the like volume of oxygen being 100. This table is now superseded by another published 2 years ago. See *Annals de Chimie*, volume 38, or Dr Henry's *Chemistry*, appendix (11th Edit.).[10]

8. The reference is to Thomson's *Attempt to Establish the First Principles of Chemistry by Experiments,* 2 vols. (1825).

9. H. Davy, *Elements of Chemical Philosophy* (1812); W. H. Wollaston, "A Synoptic Scale of Chemical Equivalents," *Philosophical Transactions of the Royal Society of London 104* (1814), 1–22.

10. William Henry's 1801 *Epitome of Chemistry,* which went through many editions and revisions.

In this new table Berzelius has given the relative atomic weights in two columns, one for the oxygen standard and the other for the hydrogen standard. The number denoting oxygen [in the] first column is 100; that denoting hydrogen in the 2nd [is 1]. The principles of the table correspond with those of Dr [Thomson] in his late publication on the atomic theory, except that [Berzelius] takes his 1 in the hydrogen scale to signify the weight of [1 volume] of hydrogen, and Dr Thomson assumes, as I have done, 1 to de [note the] weight of 1 *atom* of hydrogen. In consequence of this Be [rzelius'] numbers in the hydrogen column require [a correction factor in] order to be compared with Dr Th [omson's] . . .

[Bottom of page burnt away]

[*page* 5]

are the sole consideration; but I have doubts in several instances whether it can be allowed as one of the best tables as regards the relative weights of *atoms*.

It is not a little remarkable that such men as Berzelius, Davy and even Wollaston should contemplate a system of chemical equivalents, and not be aware that they were speculating upon the atoms or ultimate combining particles of bodies. Though they do not adopt the conclusion that chemical equivalents must necessarily be founded upon a system of atoms, they are often at fault they scarcely know why, for proper numbers to designate the ratios. (See note to Davy's *Chemistry*, page 505. I have read this repeatedly, but could never make out its meaning.[11])

In Berzelius' first table there are no double atoms or double numbers for the same article. In the last table there are about 28 double atoms out of 50 of those bodies which are generally considered as simple [or u]nitary substances. In each of these cases he affixes [one symbol] for the simple atom (generally the initial letters of its name [as given] above) and in the adjacent column the number denoting [its weight]; and immedi-

11. The page-long note explains Davy's "Mode of calculating the numbers representing the elements."

ately below he has the same symbol [with a] line through it, and adjacent to this he places the double of [the first] number. I am quite at a loss to understand the [significance] of this, unless it is to signify a doubt which of the [two numbers is] the true [weight]. Certainly these are . . .

[Bottom of page burnt away]

[*page* 6]

If I am right in my conjecture in regard to these double or doubtful weights, I cannot but observe that Berzelius has admitted a larger number than was necessary. But if it is his judgment that what he has marked as single atoms is their true weight, and likewise the double ones true weights of two atoms, then I may observe that I agree with him in regard to azote, sulphur, fluorine, carbon, tin, lead, iron, manganese, gluccinium, aluminium and sodium—but I am persuaded his double atoms of hydrogen and chlorine are designated by the weights due to single ones.

If Berzelius' notion is that the weights he has attached to iodine, boron, columbium, rhodium, uranium, zirconium, copper, and mercury are doubtful, that is doubts may exist whether the single or double weights are representative of the true weights of one atom of each of those substances, then I agree with him as regards these several articles. But with regard to his weights of phosphorus, arsenic, chromium, antimony, . . . and cobalt, I cannot assent that either his single or do [uble atoms] are near approximations to the true weights of [the articles].

At an early period of my chemical enquiries [I saw] the advantage of a chemical notation, in for [warding] my own progress, but most of all in incul [cating] elements of the science to [beginner]s. Having [taught] the principles of the atom . . .

[Bottom of page burnt away]

[*page* 7]

board, to represent not only the atoms of simple or elementary bodies, but also some of the well known and most interesting compounds; in these last the atoms were arranged according to the method exhibited in the plates to my *Chemistry,* volume 1st, part 2nd, so that all elastic particles of the same kind, as those of oxygen, hydrogen and azote were placed as far as possible from each other in the compound atom. The reasons for adopting round or globular particles to represent the elements of simple bodies, especially of elastic fluids, were given, as likewise for adopting the positions of the particles in the compound atom. All this would have been very difficult to convey to a large and promiscuous audience without [the use of] suitable diagrams.[12]

[Ber]zelius from his views of combinations was obliged [to adopt] a different notation. The difficulty of conceiving [how one] *volume* of an elastic fluid, could have one or [more *vol*]-*umes* of another elastic fluid in contact with [it wh]atever figures the volumes might be of, was so [great as to need the aid of sym]bols. The combinations must be expressed . . .

[Bottom of page burnt away]

[*page 8*]

sulphuric acid by (S̈) the letter S with three dots over it, which looks very like one atom of sulphur with three atoms of oxygen united to it ( ).

My method of denoting atomic combinations cannot be so advantageously applied where the atoms are numerous as where they are few. The arrangement cannot be made upon a plane such as it would be by nature. In such case a method somewhat like that of Berzelius might be advantageously adopted. But his method of expressing them by the initial letter of the name of the article, or in case there are several articles with the same initials, as fluor, ferrum, by the initial in one case (F for fluor) and by two or three of the first letters (Fe for ferrum) in another, tends to perplexity. It is so analogous

---

12. For Dalton's use of diagrams in his lectures, see W. W. H. Gee, H. F. Coward, and A. Harden, "John Dalton's Lectures and Lecture Illustrations," *Manchester Memoirs* 59 (1914–15), no. 12. See also Dalton's statements to the B.A.A.S., reproduced later in this chapter.

to algebraical symbols and yet so different in signification, that
any person familiar with the latter notation must be careful not
to confound them. It would be much better to have symbols
on purpose to express elem [entary] atoms, and then combinations of them might be expres [sed so] or otherwise after the
manner of Berzelius.

Part 2nd

The doctrine of definite proportions in chemistry [was]
taught by every writer on the elements of that science for more
. . . . . . The proportion of carbonic acid to li [me] in lime-
stone [was] known to be nearly as 44:56 . . . .
. . . in sulphate of p [o]t [a]sh 45:5 . . .

[Bottom of page burnt away]

[*page* 9]
placed the subject in which exhibited the relative weights of
the several acids and bases of salts. By taking 1000 parts of sulphuric acid and finding what weights of the several bases lime,
soda, potash, etc. were required to saturate that quantity of
acid, and subsequently determining what quantities of other
acids would saturate the said weights of the several bases, he established the relation of weights of all the articles in his table
that were required for mutual saturation. He found, no doubt
to his great satisfaction, that the table of weights to bases which
he had ascertained for sulphuric acid would just as well serve
for any other acids, only the quantities of those other acids
must be less or more than 1000, but when once determined by
experiment they remained constants. His table was the first
that was made of chemical equivalents, or of definite proportions, and all that has been done since, by those who use these
terms, has been to *enlarge* and *correct* his table.[13]

If Richter had pursued the subject he would have [found]
that several acids and bases have more than one [equiva]lent.
Whenever this occurred it would render [his table a]mbi-

13. Richter's table, in the form in which Dalton refers to it, was first published
in C. L. Berthollet's *Essai de Statique Chimique*, 2 vols. (Paris, 1803; English ed.
1804).

guous, except to such elements as never unite [but in one]and
the same proportion. For, if a given weight of [an acid] unites
with one, two, or more equal or unequal weights of the [same
base] how can one of these weights be said to be its equivalent
rather [than any ot]her? In such cases the most simple of the
combinations [should be] investigated if possible from the nature and properties of the . . . . always
b . . . e had to the combinations of the two . . . .
. . . . had . . . likewise. Thus in the case of azote. . .

[Bottom of page burnt away]

[*page* 10]
adverted to above, namely of azote and oxygen.

In presenting the following tables I shall adopt the number
8 to represent one atom or one equivalent of oxygen, not because I think it the most correct, but because it is frequently
met with in books of chemistry, and one number is as good as
another for illustrating the principle of the tables: and I shall
for like reasons adopt the following as the scale of ratios in the
several compounds; viz.

	Azote		*Oxygen*		*A*		*Ox*
Nitrous oxide	14	+	8	or	7	:	4
Nitrous gas	14	+	16	or	7	:	8
Subnitrous acid	14	+	24	or	7	:	12
Nitrous acid	14	+	32	or	7	:	16
Nitric acid	14	+	40	or	7	:	20

TABLE 1ST
Nitrous oxide assumed the most simple [combination]

	Azote		*Oxygen*
Nitrous oxide	14 (1 at. or equiv.)	+	8 (1 at . . .
Nitrous gas	14	+	
Subnitrous acid			

[Bottom of page burnt away]

[*page* 11]

TABLE 2D
Nitrous gas assumed the most simple combination.

	az.		ox.	atom of compound
Nitrous oxide	14 (2 at. or equiv.)	+	8 (1 at. or equiv.)	=22
Nitrous gas	7 (1 at.)	+	8 (1 at.)	=15
Subnitrous acid	14 (2 at.)	+	24 (3 at.)	=38
Nitrous acid	7 (1 at.)	+	16 (2 at.)	=23
Nitric acid	14 (2 at.)	+	40 (5 at.)	=54

TABLE 3D
Subnitrous acid assumed the most simple combination.

	az.		ox.	atom of compound
Nitrous oxide	14 (3 at. or equiv.)	+	8 (1 at. or equiv.)	=22
Nitrous gas	14 (3 at.)	+	16 (2 at.)	=30
Subnitrous acid	4⅔ (1 at. or equiv.)	+	8 (1 at. or equiv.)	=12⅔
Nitrous acid	14 (3 at.)	+	32 (4 at.)	=46
Nitric acid	14 (3 at.)	+	40 (5 at.)	=54

TABLE 4TH
Nitrous acid assumed the most simple combination.

	az.		ox.	atom of compound
Nitrous oxide	14 (4 at. or equiv.)	+	8 (1 at. or equiv.)	=22
Nitrous gas	7 (2 at.)		8 (1 at.)	15
Subnitrous acid	14 (4 at.)		24 (3 at.)	38

	az.	*ox.*	*atom of* *compound*
[Ni]trous acid	3½ (1 at.)	8 (1 at.)	11½
	at.)	40 (5 at.)	54

[Bottom of page burnt away]

[*page* 12]

Now though all these tables agree in giving the true ratios of
azote and oxygen in each case, yet the disparity in the weights
of the compound atoms and in the numbers of simple atoms
forming the compounds, is such in the 3 last tables as to shew
any one conversant with the subject, the utter improbability of
any of the three according with the usual simplicity in the laws
of combinations. It cannot be allowed that either nitrous or nitric acid presents any one feature by which they may be con-
'sidered as less complex than nitrous oxide gas. The first and
second tables are those from one of which we must trace out
the combinations of nature.

So far back as the year 1803 I had resolved in my mind the
various combinations then known of azote and oxygen, and had
determined almost without doubts, that nitrous gas is a binary
compound and nitrous oxide a ternary as may be seen in the
table of atoms published at the conclusion of my essay on the
absorption of gases by water (*Manchester Memoirs,* volume 1,
new series). Sir H. Davy in his *Elements of Chemistry* was, I
believe, the first person who adopted atomic combination as
stated in the 1st table. He was followed by Dr Wollaston
[and] by Berzelius. The last mentioned chemist had another
[reason] for following their examples; he conceived at that
time [that azote] was a compound of a metallic base and oxygen. [It would] therefore be heavier than an atom of oxygen.
[In his list] of 1814 we find azote represented by 179½, nitrous [oxide by] 279½ and nitrous gas by 379½. But lately he
has [changed his mind] entirely in regard to the combinations
of azote [with oxygen, to those] above in the 2nd table, as may
be [seen] in his [new atomic table] published in 18[2]8. . .

[Bottom of page burnt away]

[*page* 13]
observation "The weight of an atom of azote which I chose, volume 2nd page 42, for the reason there assigned, cannot, I find be reconciled to the constitution of the nitrates." Upon this he changes the weight of the azote, or makes it double of what it was before; but I have never been able to learn in any one instance that he has pointed out the particular case or cases in which the former weight is found to be irreconcileable with the nitrates. A change in the weight of one of the most important of the chemical elements should not be hastily made, and that without any specific charge against the old one, or any reason in favour of the new. Dr Wollaston had just before published the same hypothetical view, in his account of the scale of chemical equivalents.

Dr Thomson, and most British chemists after him, seem to consider equivalents as synonymous with atoms; but Dr Wollaston did not acknowledge them as such; he seems to consider atoms as an ulterior investigation. Gay-Lussac and the leading French chemists adopt the language of volumes combining; though they do not acknowledge those volumes as significant [of atoms.] Not that they deny the existence of atoms and their combinations, [but] they go no further than the expressions of facts. In both cases [one] is doing these authors injustice to represent them as [rejecting] atoms.

[On the] whole it appears that Berzelius and I are the only chemists [who agree] with each other in regard to the atomic compounds of azote [and] that the majority of British chemists are at variance with [us regarding] those compounds. I may add that I entertain no . . . . ultimate . . . adopted. . . .

[Bottom of page burnt away]

[*page* 14]
its constitution to be 4 atoms of sulphate of alumine united to one of sulphate of potash with 30 atoms of water. In the 2nd volume of the same work I concluded alum to be 1 atom bisulphate of potash united to 3 of sulphate of alumine. This conclusion, I have since found, is not correct. On making a new se-

ries of experiments in the present year (1830) I have seen
reason to adopt a new view of the subject. It has occurred
chiefly by a comparison of the red sulphate of iron with the sulphate of alumine. I was not aware at the time that Berzelius
had adopted the same opinion, and I apprehend from similar
reasons, but I have only his table of 1828 and an observation of
Dr Turner's in the 3rd edition of his *Chemistry* [14] for authority. Berzelius long ago demonstrated that the red sulphate of
iron required as many atoms of sulphuric acid as there were
atoms of oxygen in the base to form [a] perfect salt; or that an
atom of red sulphate consisted [of] 3 atoms of sulphuric acid
and 3 of oxygen to 2 of iron. [By] analogy I conclude that 1
atom of sulphate of alumine [consists of] 3 atoms of sulphuric
acid and 3 of oxygen with 2 of . . .   . . . (the metal), this combination of 3 oxygen with 2 atoms . . .   . . . constituting one
atom of alumine (the earth) or oxide of the . . .   . . . to the red
oxide of iron.

Alum, on this view of the subject, will . . .   . of
sulphate of potash united to . . . atom . . .   .
. . . and one atom of aluminium . . .

[Bottom of page burnt away]

[*page* 15]
by the addition of more base, so as not to affect the colour.

2nd They both will dissolve nearly 50 per cent more of base
than they can retain; but in time an insoluble sub-salt is
formed and the solution resumes its original character.

3rd Both bases refuse to unite with carbonic acid.

4th One atom of each of these bases requires 3 atoms of other
acids, as well as the sulphuric, to form the several salts.

5th They both indicate excess of acid, by putting any base to
a solution of the salts, when it will be dissolved, but not long
retained, shewing the excess of acid to be essential to the per-
manency of the combinations.

6th In a mixture of the solutions of red sulphate of [iron]
green sulphate of iron and sulphate of alumine [the] lime

14. E. Turner, *Elements of Chemistry,* 3rd ed. (1831).

water throws down the red oxide [of iron] mixed or combined with less or more alumine . . . . . . throws down alumine, and lastly the green . . . . . . oxide of iron, showing that this compound . . . . . . is precipitated before the protoxide.[15]

DALTON AND THE ROYAL INSTITUTION, 1803–1804

As Dalton is known to have made his first particle weight measurements in the autumn of 1803, considerable interest attaches to the course of twenty lectures he delivered in London at the close of the year. That Dalton discussed his ideas on chemical combination with Humphry Davy is apparent both from his notebooks [16] and from the paper reproduced above. However, these ideas do not seem to have featured prominently in the lectures. Neither Dalton's notes nor a complete syllabus for the course are now available, but a fair picture of the lectures can still be pieced together. Reproduced below are a letter Dalton wrote before setting off to London, a Royal Institution handbill, and extracts from letters composed immediately after the course was over.

The letter Dalton wrote before setting off to London is as follows:

Manchester, November 24th, 1803

Respected Friend,

I received your letter containing the agreement of the Committee to my proposition.

As it will not be convenient for me to be in town before the 17th or 18th of next month, I should be glad to know previously whether my accommodation as to board and lodging would be in the Institution; if not whether you know of any place in the vicinity where the same could probably be procured. It will be necessary for me to spend a considerable portion of time to make myself acquainted with the structure and

15. Manuscript in possession of the Manchester Literary and Philosophical Society.
16. See the entries reproduced in Roscoe and Harden, *New View*, pp. 43–44.

use of some of the apparatus; and therefore I am the more solicitous on the above head. Pray what is the usual duration of a
lecture, 1 or 2 hours?

An immediate reply to these enquiries will much oblige,

Yours respectfully,

J. Dalton.[17]

[On back of sheet:]

The following heads of the first 4 lectures will probably be
wanted before my arrival:

1. *Introductory.* Objects of natural philosophy. Division of
the science. Utility of the study. Plan of the lectures.

2. *Properties of Matter.* Extension. Impenetrability. Divisibility. Inertia. Various species of attraction and repulsion. *Motion.* Forces. Composition of forces. Collision. *Pendulums.*

3. *Projectiles.* Resistance of the air. *Mechanic powers.*
Strength of timber, etc.

4. *Pneumatics.* Nature of elastic fluids. The atmosphere. Air
pump. Spring and weight of the air proved by experiments. Barometer.

Information on the final part of the course is contained in a
Royal Institution handbill, which reads as follows:

23rd January, 1804

Royal Institution

The following lectures will be delivered this, and the following week.

Monday, 23rd January, at 8 o'Clock. Mr Dalton.

Constitution of mixed gases. Simple elastic fluid, how consti-

17. Addressed to Mr. N. Savage [Clerk and Printer to the Royal Institution],
Royal Institution, Albemarle Street, London. Ms. in possession of the Royal Institution. These lectures also have a somewhat different interest. In the summer of
1803 the Royal Institution was itself in difficulty. Thomas Young having abruptly
resigned his professorship. It was to Dalton as a man of "known talents and reputation" that the Managers turned in this emergency. His lectures on "mechanics and
physics" opened the new season at the Royal Institution: it is probable that Dalton
was being actively considered to fill the vacant professorship of natural philosophy.
(See *Minutes of the Meeting of Managers of the Royal Institution*, III, 151, 167,
170, and 172.)

tuted. Equilibrium of mixed elastic fluids. Aqueous vapour. The atmosphere.
Tuesday, 24th January, at 2 o'Clock. Mr Allen.
   Introductory. Reasoning by induction. Theory. Hypothesis. General properties of matter. Laws of motion.
Wednesday, 25th January, at 2 o'Clock. Mr Dalton.
   Meteorology. Object of the science. Barometer. Thermometer. Hygrometer. Rain. Hail. Snow. Dew. Clouds. Fiery meteors. General observations. Conclusion of the course.

―――――――

Tuesday, 31st January, at 2 o'Clock. Mr Allen.
   Moving forces. Elasticity. Composition of motion. Uniform, accelerated, and retarded motion. Pendulums. Projectiles.
Thursday, 2nd February, at 2 o'Clock. Mr Davy.
   Introductory. View of the objects of the two courses of chemistry. Relations of chemistry to natural changes. The objects of the chemistry of artificial operations. General ideas concerning the utility and advantages of the study.
Saturday, 4th February, at 2 o'Clock. Mr Davy.
   Chemistry in its connection with artificial operations. General views of the subject. Attraction. Experiments on its agencies, and on the laws by which it is governed.[18]

Thus definite information is available on the first four and last two of the twenty lectures. It also appears that the eighteenth lecture was on heat (see below). Of the remaining thirteen all that is known with certainty is that they "covered a wide range and included mechanics, electricity, magnetism, optics, astronomy, use of the globes, sound." [19]
How Dalton treated the middle section of his course may be conjectured by reference to his 1805 Manchester syllabus (he claimed that these lectures were similar to the London ones). Two letters he wrote in February 1804 confirm the improbability of this section having included particle weights. The letters well

18. Handbill in possession of the Science Museum, London.
19. Gee, Coward, and Harden, "Dalton's Lectures," p. 4.

complement the information available in the handbill given
above. The first says that:

The scientific part of the audience was wonderfully taken with
some of my original notions relative to heat, the gases, etc.,
some of which had not before been published . . . my eighteenth, on heat and the laws of expansion, etc., was received
with the greatest applause, with very few experiments. The one
that followed, was on *mixed elastic fluids,* in which I had an
opportunity of developing my ideas, that have already been
published on the subject, more fully. The doctrine has, as I ap-
prehended it would, excited the attention of philosophers
throughout Europe . . . I saw my successor, William Allen,
fairly launched; he gave his first lecture on Tuesday preceding
my conclusion.

There is no mention of laws of combination or of a "curious
theory of atoms" as being a significant part of Dalton's course or
an object of controversy. The second letter reinforces this impression. It simply says "My lately published essays on gases, etc., together with the more recent ones read at our Society, and of
which I gave the result in my late lectures, have drawn the attention of most of the philosophers of Europe." [20]
    Finally, in connection with the 1803–04 Royal Institution lec-
tures, it is interesting to notice that their success apparently led to
an early invitation to Dalton to return. This is clear from a letter
now in the Institution's possession:

Kendal, July 14, 1804

Respected Friend,
    A few days ago I received a letter from Dr Percival, contain-
ing a paragraph from your communication to him, affecting

20. From a 1 February 1804 letter to Jonathan Dalton, and a 26 February 1804
letter, quoted in W. C. Henry, *Memoirs of the Life and Scientific Researches of
John Dalton* (1854), pp. 48 and 50.

me. In reply may [I] observe that I conceive myself honored by the repeated attention of the managers of the Royal Institution. I shall be glad if my occasional services can promote their laudable views. It would probably be as convenient to me, as well as agreeable to the managers, to give 6 lectures in the last 3 weeks of January. The subjects to be certain parts of natural philosophy which have been more immediately my study, as heat, physical elements, elastic fluids and meteorology.

I must however observe that my health at present, and for some time past, has been such as to preclude me from the sanguine prosecution of my philosophical speculations. I am now spending a week or two in the country on account of my health, I hope to some advantage. If on the decline of the year my health should take an unfavourable turn, it will be my care to apprize you of it in time, so that the Institution may not suffer from my inability.

I remain sincerely,
Your obliged friend,
John Dalton.[21]

It is not clear why this proposed course did not take place. Certainly it was not on account of Dalton's ill-health, as he visited London to purchase apparatus early in 1805.[22]

THE 1805 AND 1807 LECTURES

It has long been known that Dalton gave his first Manchester lectures in the spring of 1805, and the prospectus he drew up inviting subscriptions to the course has been published.[23] However the actual content of the lectures was unknown until a copy of the printed syllabus recently came to light. This syllabus, which is of great interest for the way it reflects Dalton's

21. Addressed to T. Bernard ["Visitor" of the Royal Institution]. Ms. in possession of the Royal Institution.
22. Roscoe and Harden, New Yiew, pp. 66–67.
23. Gee, Coward, and Harden, "Dalton's Lectures," p. 4.

thinking at a crucial stage in the development of his ideas, is given in full below.

No information is available on what Dalton said about his "original ideas on the division of matter into elements and their composition" (Lecture 1). It is interesting that the section on combination only covers gases and that considerable prominence is given to the compounds of carbon. Of interest also is the discussion of "Absorption of gases by water" (Lecture 17) which shows little evidence of particle weights being mentioned, in contrast to the 1803 paper to the "Lit and Phil." Notice should also be taken of Lectures 13 and 14 "On heat," as they show well the sort of general laws that Dalton loved to discover.

Syllabus
of
A Course of Lectures
on
Natural Philosophy.
By *John Dalton*
Manchester:
Printed by S. Russell, Deansgate.
1805

Lectures 1 and 2.
On Matter, Motion and Mechanic Principles. Introduction.
General properties of matter—Extension—Divisibility—
original ideas on the division of matter into elements and their
composition—Solidity—Mobility—Inertia—Gravitation and
the various species of attraction—Laws of motion—uniform
and accelerated motion illustrated by Atwood's machine. Centripetal and centrifugal forces—Centre of gravity—Laws of
percussion—Composition of motion—Projectiles—Pendulums
—Mechanic powers—Strength and stress of timber, etc.

Lecture 3.
Hydrostatics.—Fluids of two kinds, elastic and inelastic—
illustration—tenacity of fluids. Properties of inelastic fluids,

such as water-pressure is as the depth-rise to the same level—
heights of different fluids pressing against each other, inversely
as their specific gravities—floating bodies. Specific gravities of
bodies—solids—liquids, how found—Hydrometer—
Gravimeter, &c.

Lectures 4 and 5.

Pneumatics. Atmosphere a mixture of elastic fluids, illustration of it—Air-pump—various experiments shewing the spring
and weight of the air. Barometer—Resistance of the air—
Sound—Air in water, &c. Ebullition.
Fountains—Condensation of the air as the pressure, &c.

Lecture 6.

Hydraulic and Pneumatic Instruments.—Suction—Syphon
—Tantalus' cup—Ebbing and flowing wells—Pumps, Hydro-
static bellows—motion of water through pipes—Jets—Capillary
attraction—Filter, &c.

Lectures 7, 8 and 9.

Electricity and Galvanism.—History of Electricity—Electric
attraction and repulsion—Positive and negative electricity—
Conductors and electrics—Description of the electric machine
—Experiments on attraction and repulsion—Theory and illus-
tration of the Leyden phial or electric Jar—Electrometers—
Medical electricity—Miscellaneous experiments—Inflammation
of combustible bodies—Electric battery and experiments with
it to fuse metals, &c.—Thunder and lightning illustrated—
Electrophorus—Luminous appearances in the dark, &c.—
Galvanism, history of it, and principal phenomena.

Lecture 10.

Magnetism.—Magnetic attraction and repulsion, peculiar to
iron and steel—Principal phenomena—polarity—mariner's
compass—variation, annual and diurnal—affected by the Aurora Borealis—Dipping needle—Communication of
magnetism—Theory.

Lectures 11 and 12.

Optics.—Nature and properties of light—direct vision—
Catoptrics, or vision by reflection—Mirrors, plane concave and

convex—Dioptrics, or vision by refraction—Lenses plane, concave and convex—Colours—Description of the eye—Manner
of vision—Various optical instruments exhibited and
explained.—Rainbow.

Lectures 13 and 14.

On Heat.—Importance of heat in the system of nature—
Heat an elastic fluid—Capacities of various bodies for heat, or
specific heats—Expansion of solids by heat—law unknown—of
liquids, as the square of the temperature from their freezing
points—of elastic fluids, as the cube of the temperature from
absolute cold.—Thermometer—lowest point of heat.—Force
of steam from all liquids in geometrical progression to increments of temperature in arithmetical progression, consequently
represented truly by the ordinates of the logarithmic curve.—
Refrigeration of bodies—Radiation, and reflection of heat.

Lecture 15.

On the Elements of Bodies and their Composition.—
Consideration of the divisibility of matter resumed—Assumptions, that an ultimate particle of water is composed of one of
hydrogen and one of oxygen, and that one of ammoniac is
formed of one of azote and one of hydrogen,—reasons for the
assumption—consequently that nitrous gas is composed of one
of azote and one of oxygen, nitrous oxide of two azote and one
oxygen, nitric acid of one azote and two oxygen, and nitrous acid
of one nitric acid and one nitrous gas—Agreement of these conclusions with the phenomena—Carbon or charcoal and its combinations—

One charcoal and one oxygen—carbonic oxide
One charcoal and two oxygen—carbonic acid
One charcoal and one hydrogen—olefiant gas
One charcoal and two hydrogen—carburetted hydrogen
    from stagnant water, etc., etc.

Lecture 16.

On Mixed Elastic Fluids and the Atmosphere.—Invisibility
of all elastic fluids—Great difference in their specific gravity—
No two when mixed separate again by gravity—reason of this

commonly ascribed to a slight chemical affinity—objections to this explanation.—New theory explained, which considers the particles of gases only repulsive of their own kind—illustration of it by the gradual diffusion of all gases throughout one another, and by the extraction of one gas from others by a body possessing an affinity for it.—The atmosphere a mixture of at least four simple atmospheres; namely, azotic gas, oxygenous, carbonic acid and aqueous vapour.

Lecture 17.

On the Absorption of Gases by Water, &c.—Water commonly contains air,—recent discovery that the quantity of air is as the pressure on the surface—When a mixture of gases are incumbent on water, each gas presses distinctly on the surface, proved by the quantity absorbed and retained in the water—Different gases are absorbable in different degrees.—Water takes its bulk of carbonic acid, sulphuretted hydrogen and nitrous oxide—1/8 of its bulk of olefiant gas—1/27 of its bulk of oxygenous, carburetted hydrogen and nitrous gases—1/64 of its bulk of hydrogen, azote and carbonic oxide—about 1/50 of common air—Theory of the absorption—Nature of ebullition —Air being chemically combined with water, unfounded.

Lecture 18.

Meteorology.—The phenomena of meteorology; namely, winds, temperature, clouds, rain, hail, snow, dew—evaporation —various fiery meteors, considered and explained with experimental illustrations—Instruments of meteorology, &c.

Lectures 19 and 20.

Astronomy.—Introduction—Solar system illustrated by the Orrery, &c.—Phenomena of the earth and moon more particularly by the Tellurian—Eclipses—Laws of motion of the Planets explained by the whirling table—Tides—System of the universe—Reflections.[24]

The real widening of Dalton's ideas on particle weights, and their application to the whole of chemistry, took place in the

24. Syllabus in possession of the Manchester Literary and Philosophical Society.

period between his Manchester (Spring 1805) and Edinburgh lectures (Spring 1807). The syllabus of the latter series, given below, contrasts sharply with the Manchester one of two years earlier. The Edinburgh course had the support of Thomas Thomson, the influential Scottish chemist. A recently discovered letter in which Dalton solicited Thomson's aid in arranging the lectures is given in chapter 7. The following advertisement from the *Edinburgh Evening Courant* of 28 March, 1807 shows that the course actually took place in Thomson's classroom:

Lectures on Heat And Chemical Elements
J. Dalton of Manchester, intends to deliver a course of five lectures on heat and chemical elements. The first lecture will be given on Thursday the 2nd of April, at seven o'clock in the evening, at Dr Thomson's Class Room, High School Yards. Subscriptions to the course, *Half-a-Guinea*. The names of subscribers may be entered, further particulars seen, and tickets procured, at the shops of Messrs. Constable & Co., Cross; Guthrie and Tate, Nicholson Street; and Blackwood's, South Bridge. Reid's Lodgings, No. 99, Nicholson Street; March 27, 1807.

The syllabus was as follows (see Figure 5):

Syllabus
of a
Course of Lectures on Heat,
and
Chemical Elements
By John Dalton

Lectures I. & II.—*On Heat.*
Introduction:—Heat an elastic fluid,—mode of its combination with bodies analogous to an atmosphere of air surrounding a planet;—some bodies possessed of a stronger attraction for heat than others, hence their different capacities for heat; —the same body never changes its capacity abruptly, without,

at the same time, changing its form.—Ice, Water, and Vapour.
—Theory of the formation of Ice, accounting for the expansion
and the angle of crystallization:—Reason of the expansion of
water before congelation.—Temperature considered;—Are
equal gradations of temperature in a body produced by equal
increments of heat? No; unless the bulk of the body remains
constant:—Proof of this assertion from air,—from water.—
State of heat in a perfect vacuum;—density of it, in that state, a
proper measure of temperature.—Radiation of heat the same
in vacuo as in elastic fluid.—Mercurial thermometers inaccurate on two accounts:—New graduation proposed, founded on
the supposition that the expansive force of air increases in geometrical progression with equal increments of heat.—
Expansive force of the vapour of water, ether, &c., in geometrical progression, conformable to this law.—Expansion of water,
mercury, &c. as the square of the temperature from the point of
greatest density, also conformable to this graduation.—
Newtonian law of the refrigeration of bodies conformable to
this new graduation.—Reason of the decrease of temperature
in ascending into the atmosphere.

Account of a series of Experiments to find the absolute quantity of Heat in bodies, by four different processes, nearly agree-
ing in their results—lowest point about 2000 deg. below freezing water—Review of Lavoisier's Experiments on the
Calorimeter: Account of the result of a series of Experiments to
determine the Heat produced by the combustion of 12 species
of combustible bodies performed with a very simple apparatus,
—Comparison of these results with those of Lavoisier,—Great
capacity of oxygenous Gas for Heat, &c.

———————

Lectures III. IV. & V.
of Chemical Elements.

Elastic Fluids conceived to consist of indivisible particles or
atoms of matter, surrounded with atmospheres of Heat.—
Liquid and solid bodies conceived likewise to be composed of
atoms surrounded with Heat, but in a state of much greater

proximity, by virtue of the attraction of aggregation.—Reasons for believing, that in the Chemical Union of Elementary Principles, we shall generally, if not always, find a compound, consisting of 1 atom of each.—That the next most simple combination is 1 atom with 2.—That such combinations always take place before more complex ones, which in reality do rarely occur. Water, 1 atom of oxygen and 1 of hydrogen; Ammoniac, 1 atom of azote and 1 of hydrogen; Nitrous Gas, 1 atom of azote and 1 of oxygen; Nitric Acid, 1 azote and 2 oxygen; Nitrous Oxide, 1 azote and 2 oxygen, &c. coincidences of these with experimental results. Carbonic Oxide, 1 charcoal and 1 oxygen; Carbonic Acid, 1 charcoal and 2 oxygen, Olefiant Gas, 1 charcoal and 1 hydrogen; Carburetted Hydrogen, 1 charcoal and 2 hydrogen, &c. &c.,—Weights of the ultimate particles of Acids, Alkalis, Earths, and Metals. Theory of Metallic Oxides; that the Protoxide is 1 atom of metal and 1 of oxygen; the Deutoxide is 1 metal and 2 oxygen, &c.—Application of these principles to the composition of Neutral Salts, as Carbonates, Sulphates, Nitrates, Muriates, &c. in which it will be shewn, that the Theory accords with the most correct Experiments hitherto performed, either exactly or within 2 per cent.—Carbonates, &c. are 1 carbonic acid and 1 base; Subcarbonates, &c. are 1 acid and 2 base; Supercarbonates, &c. are 2 acid and 1 base, &c.[25]

The syllabus shows that in these lectures Dalton covered a far wider range of chemical problems than he was able to include in the 1808 "Part I" of his *New System of Chemical Philosophy*. But the debt of the *New System* to these lectures, as well as to the "Lit and Phil," was made clear in its partial dedication "To the professors of the universities, and other residents, of Edinburgh and Glasgow, who gave their attention and encouragement to the lectures on heat and chemical elements, delivered in those cities in 1807."

25. Syllabus in possession of the Manchester Literary and Philosophical Society.

THE 1835 MEETING OF THE BRITISH ASSOCIATION FOR THE ADVANCEMENT OF SCIENCE

Dalton's chemical atomic theory was a matter of lively debate for many years after its first publication. As time went on, chemists were increasingly embarrassed by the obvious practical utility of a system with such dubious philosophical foundations. A cautious empiricism or positivism became the order of the day. The manuscript reproduced at the beginning of this chapter shows that Dalton was by no means unaware of early critics and their doubts about the ontological status of his atoms. His "naive realist" view of the importance of thinking structurally and three-dimensionally was to be posthumously vindicated over the cautious, doubting empiricism favored by the majority of chemists. It is thus paradoxical and fascinating to see how, at the time, Dalton's critics had the better of the argument.

Continental chemists, from J. J. Berzelius onwards, tended to accept the great utility of Dalton's work on atomic weights and combining proportions, while rejecting his symbolism and doubting the literal validity of the atomic theory. In Britain matters were less straightforward. On the one hand there was more awareness of and sympathy for, if not agreement with, the philosophical assumptions which underlay Dalton's work. On the other hand, no British chemist remotely approached Dalton's stature in the years immediately following the deaths of W. H. Wollaston and Humphry Davy. And it was in those years that the issue of chemical symbolism became acute in Britain. Agreed symbols and agreed atomic (or equivalent) weights were urgently necessary if British chemists were to communicate with each other and take advantage of the rapid advances occurring in France and Germany.

The natural vehicle of debate was the infant British Association for the Advancement of Science. Within it Dalton occupied a commanding position as practical chemist and also as talisman and ideal type. The debate was thus a delicate affair, particularly as younger chemists were rapidly realizing the necessity of alignment with Continental example. The issue began to shape up at the inaugural meeting in York, at Dalton's own request. In October 1831 the Association's vice-president informed William Whewell (then Cambridge Professor of Mineralogy) that subcommittees for "several subjects of scientific enquiry of much importance in chemistry, geology, meteorology and natural philosophy have been proposed, and several persons have undertaken to pursue them who may be expected to execute them well; thus Dalton has insisted on more accurate and multiplied experiments to establish the primary data of chemistry and will take a part in them." The following March he also wrote to C. G. B. Daubeny, the Oxford Professor of Chemistry, that "I hope you will apply to all the really good chemists of your acquaintance to contribute to the elucidation of the chemical questions which are before us, especially Dalton's." [26]

In due course a committee on chemical notation was formally constituted. It had as chairman one of the younger chemists, Edward Turner, professor at the London University. After careful enquiry, the members of the committee reported in 1835, and they inevitably disagreed with Dalton. That even so they left him quite unrepentant is apparent from the following exchange, published in the official *Report* of the 1835 Dublin meeting of the British Association for the Advancement of Science (page 207):

Report of the Committee on Chemical Notation
Dr Turner, the Chairman of the Committee appointed to take into consideration the adoption of an uniform system of chemical notation, made a report to the following effect:—
1st. That the majority of the Committee concur in approv-

26. W. Vernon Harcourt to W. Whewell. Undated [October 1831] letter. Trinity College, Cambridge. Add. Mss. a 205 f 123; also Harcourt to C. G. B. Daubeny, 8 March 1832 letter. Magdalen College, Oxford. Mss. 400, item 12.

ing of the employment of that system of notation which is already in general use on the Continent, though there exist among them some differences of opinion on points of detail.

2ndly. That they think it desirable not to deviate in the manner of notation from algebraic usage except so far as convenience requires.

3rdly. That they are of opinion that it would save much confusion if every chemist would always state explicitly the exact *quantities* which he intends to represent by his symbols.

Dr Dalton stated to the Chemical Section his reasons for preferring the symbols which he had himself used from the commencement of the atomic theory in 1803 to the Berzelian system of notation subsequently introduced. In his opinion regard must be had to the arrangement and equilibrium of the atoms (especially elastic atoms) in every compound atom, as well as to their number and weights. A system either of *arrangements* without *weights,* or of *weights* without *arrangements,* he considered only half of what it should be.

In stressing the importance of "arrangement and equilibrium of the atoms" Dalton revealed how much his different theories of mixed gases continued to condition his thinking about atomic theory, as late as 1835. Naïve realism, a conviction of the importance of structural chemistry, a highly pictorial imagination, and his considerable obstinacy also played important roles. A better sense of his briefly noted objection, and his critics' combination of personal deference and professional unease, may be gained from a second much fuller account. The report in the little known and scarce *Proceedings of the Fifth Meeting of the British Association for the Advancement of Science* (Dublin, 1835, see pp. 82–83) also provides a fuller picture of the excitement and importance of the encounter:

Section B. Chemistry and Mineralogy
Dr Dalton next brought forward his views of the nature of

the atomic theory, which appeared to excite great interest, as, in addition to those who usually attended this Section, we noticed very many of the leading members of the Physical, Statistical, and other Sections present. Dr Dalton had prepared a lithographic plan of his arrangement, and showed how the molecules of bodies may be considered grouped so as to represent compound atoms, (for which see Appendix. [here reproduced as Figure 7]). He stated that he considered this method as the only one representing nature, and that if the British Association sanctioned the adoption of the notation of Berzelius, as was desired by many Irish and British chemists, it would virtually have placed an extinguisher upon itself.

Professor Whewell stated, that reserving all due respect to the opinions of Dr Dalton, to whom, as the discoverer of the atomic theory, the admiration of all chemists for all ages must be necessarily awarded, yet he should declare, that he considered it impossible, in the present state of science, to rest satisfied with the arrangement of Dr Dalton. The chemists of all other nations had fallen into the views of Berzelius. The right, and what was more, the power, of priority was vested in Berzelius, and the only effect of our keeping back would be, to throw us behind science. Moreover, Dr Dalton's method supposes a theory, Berzelius only states a fact. The notation of the Swedish chemist shows that such and so many atoms are present. Dr Dalton's, on the other hand, attempts to show their method of molecular arrangement, of which we have no positive knowledge whatsoever.

Dr Kane was glad to find that the question of chemical notation had been brought before the Section in such a manner, and would venture but few observations. The necessity for notation in chemistry was now universally admitted, and the only question lay between the systems of Berzelius and of Dalton. To represent the existing state of chemical science we must have formulae of two kinds, one representing merely the result of analysis, giving the relative number and nature of the atoms composing a body, the second exhibiting the actual number

7. Dalton's 1835 Table of Atomic Symbols. From a lithograph prepared for the 1835 Dublin meeting of the B.A.A.S. (Courtesy of the Trustees of the British Museum.)

and the mode of grouping of these atoms. These are the empirical and the rational formulae, the former representing absolute fact, the latter particular theory. Now he (Dr. Kane) objected to Dr Dalton's views that they necessarily involved his own theoretical ideas, as in the instances of alcohol and ether of acetic acid, pyroacetic spirit and pyroxylic spirit, the compounds of phosphorus, &c. Whilst the notation of Berzelius being merely letters, capable of indefinite combination, can be used by all chemists, each to express his own peculiar views, which thus become universally intelligible.

Mr Babbage rose to state, that the object of chemists in this discussion was not to impugn the truth of the great law of nature discovered by Dr Dalton, but to consider the most fitting language in which to clothe it, so that it should be understood and appreciated by all. The language employed by Dr Dalton, although adopted to explain the simpler combinations of substances, became quite insufficient when much more extended relations were to be discussed. There must, therefore, arrive a period at which it must be given up, and it would be highly inexpedient to have two systems of signs for one object. He was glad to find that the tables of chemical constants, that Professor Johnston had been requested last year to draw up, had been executed in a manner so creditable to that gentleman and to the Association; and he hailed their appearance as the first of the constants of nature and art, in the publication of which he himself took such interest.

Professor Johnston stated that he was happy that the manner in which he had executed that task had proved satisfactory to the Section. He would only make one remark on the subject of notation, but that one he considered of importance. The method of symbols proposed by Dr Dalton might, perhaps, apply to the simple cases of combination that had been selected by that philosopher as examples, but when they come to be applied to groups consisting of 40, or 60, or 100 molecules, how could the eye recognize at a glance their method of arrangement. There might be a rivalry between the systems of notation in cases of binary or ternary combination, but when we come to embody all our existing knowledge in formulae, the system of Berzelius must be made use of, because it is the only one that can possibly be applied.

To Dalton, his method of employing three-dimensional formulae was in all seriousness "the only one representing nature." Like everyone who failed to grasp and endorse the theories of mixed gases which lay behind Dalton's beliefs, William Whewell had to object that "we have no positive knowledge whatsoever" of molecular arrangements. In this he was strictly correct. His own and similar views clearly carried the day. What these critics failed to see was the eventual necessity and power of an approach such as Dalton's, when discussing those molecules about which they were most cautious. The same failure is apparent in Charles Daubeny's tactful attempt to reconcile the antagonists, in his presidential address to the Association the following year (*Report* of the 1836 Bristol meeting, pp. xxix–xxxi):

On the subject of chemistry, our transactions of this year contain only a short report by Dr Turner, explanatory of the sentiments of the members of the Committee which had been appointed the preceding year, to consider whether or not it would be possible to recommend some uniform system of notation which, coming forward under the sanction of the most distinguished British chemists, might obtain universal recognition. In the discussion which took place when this subject was brought before us at Dublin, three systems of notation were proposed, differing one from the other no less in principle than in the end proposed by their adoption.

The first was that suggested by the venerable founder of the atomic theory, Dr Dalton, who aimed at expressing by his mode of notation, not merely the number of atoms of each ingredient which unite to form a given compound, but likewise the very mode of their union, the supposed collocation of the different particles respectively one to the other. He proposed, therefore, a sort of pictorial representation of each compound which he specified, just as in the infancy of writing each substance was indicated, not by an arbitrary character, but by a sign bearing some remote resemblance to the object itself. This therefore, may be denominated the hieroglyphical mode of chemical notation; it was of great use in the infancy of the atomic theory, in familiarizing the minds of men of science to the mode in which combinations take place, and thus paved a more ready way to the reception of this important doctrine. Even now it may have its advantages in conveying to the mind of a learner a clearer notion of the number and relation of the elements of a compound body one to the other; and in those which consist only of two or three elements a symbolic representation after Dr Dalton's plan might be nearly as concise as any other. But it would be difficult, consistently with brevity, to express in this manner any of those more complicated combinations that meet us in every stage of modern chemical enquiry, as for instance in the compounds of cyanogen, or in the proximate principles of organic life.

The second mode of notation is that, in which the method adopted in algebra is applied to meet the purposes of chemistry. This method, whilst it is recommended by its greater perspicuity, and by its being intelligible to all educated persons, has the advantage also of involving no hypothesis, and being equally available by individuals who may have taken up the most opposite views of the collocation of the several atoms, or who dismiss the question as altogether foreign to their consideration. This, therefore, may be compared to the alphabetical mode of writing in use amongst civilized nations; the characters indeed may differ, the words formed by a combination of these characters may be very various, but the principles on which they are put together to express certain sounds and ideas are in all countries the same.

The third method of notation, which has been recommended by the authority of several great Continental chemists, and especially of Berzelius, resembles rather a system of short-hand than one of ordinary writing; its express object being to abbreviate, so far as is consistent with perspicuity, the mode of notation last described. But although most chemists may find it convenient to employ some of these abbreviated forms of expression, it seems doubtful whether any particular amount of them can be recommended for general adoption, since the necessity for it will vary according to the habits of the individual, the nature of his inquiries, and the objects for which his notes are designed.

A chemist, for example, the character of whose mind enables him quickly to perceive, and clearly to recollect minute distinctions, may find a much more abbreviated style of notation convenient, than would be at all advisable to others; one who is engaged in the analysis of organic compounds will be more sensible of the utility of such symbols, than another who is conversant chiefly with a less complicated class of combinations; and one who notes down the results of his experiments for the benefit of private reference, and not with any immediate view to others, may indulge in a more concise and complex system of notation, than would be convenient, where either of the latter objects were contemplated.

As the shortest road is proverbially not always the most expeditious, so in chemical notation more time may often be lost in correcting our own blunders and those of the compositor, where dots and commas of many sorts are introduced in the place of initial letters to express certain elements, than was gained by the more compendious method of expression employed. Add to which, in the preference given to one set of dots over another, or in the particular collocation of them, above, below, or at the side of, the symbol to which they are referred, we have no fixed principle to guide us, and can therefore only be determined by the greater or less frequent adoption of one method than of another.

Perhaps, therefore, all that can be hoped from a committee of British chemists would be, to set forward the various uses of some system of chemical notation, the purposes for which each of those brought before them seems chiefly applicable, and the degree of prevalence which one has obtained over the rest.

If I may be allowed to offer my own humble opinion on a point which has been so much debated amongst British chemists, I should remark, that for the purpose of rendering more intelligible to beginners the mode in which various bodies are supposed to combine, the Daltonian method of notation may be of use, just as pictorial representation often comes in aid of verbal description to convey the idea of a complex object; but that where the design is to state in the clearest and least hypothetical terms, the nature of a series of combinations, a mode of notation as closely as possible approaching to that adopted in algebra seems preferable—remembering always, that as in algebra we omit certain signs for the sake of greater brevity, so it may be allowable to do in applying its principles to chemistry; these abbreviations being of course the most advisable in cases, where, by reason of the greater number of elements involved, the expression of them at whole length would occupy so much space, as to prevent the whole from being comprehended at a glance.

Thus Dalton was left bloody if unbowed, his ideas pejoratively considered only as "of great use in the infancy of the atomic theory." Time alone could reveal that his views on structure possessed a power far beyond his critics' perceptions. Precisely the sort of three-dimensional thinking he pioneered was to prove vital not only to the spectacular progress of organic chemistry in the late nineteenth century, but also to the triumphs of molecular biology in our own time.

7. John Dalton's Scientific Correspondence

As I expect my Essays will merit
the attention of the curious, they
may possibly circulate pretty rapidly.
John Dalton in 1793

THE SIGNIFICANCE OF THE LETTERS

It is one of the ironies of history that Humphry Davy, a man of bold theoretical speculations, should be remembered largely for his practical achievements (decomposition of the fixed alkalies, the safety lamp) while John Dalton, a man of more restrained imagination but great practical perseverance, should be honored chiefly for his atomic *theory*. Dalton's limitations, and the contrast with Davy, were well brought out in a revealing private letter from his first biographer, W. C. Henry, to John Davy, Humphry's brother and memorialist:

> 1 Den Terrace, Teignmouth
> Sep 14 [1853?]

My Dear Sir,

I now enclose all the letters from Sir H. Davy, which I have discovered among Dalton's papers. You will see, that I have copied two in extenso, and extracted a passage from a third. Should you see any reason to object to their publication, which however I do not anticipate, I shall of course be governed by your wishes. I find occasional mention of the Taylor family, especially of Miss Taylor of Moston, who was a favourite pupil of Dr Dalton's and an accomplished mathematician.

I am much in want of personal anecdotes to diversify the monotony of an analysis of one scientific memoir after another. Dalton's life was emphatically uneventful. His range of interest did not extend much beyond the compass of the physical sciences, and there was a quaintness and dryness in his style, and an insensibility to literary excellence, which restrains his biographer within narrow limits. You had a grander subject for your admirably filled canvas, and "che sovra gli altri, come aquila vola."

In perusing again, after the lapse of many years, the 2nd part of the 1st volume of Dalton's *New System,* I am deeply impressed with his deficiencies as an *experimentalist,* and with his reluctance to admit the potassium and chlorine theories of your brother, and the law of volumes. This last is scarcely explicable in one who was in the habit of looking upon all empirical phenomena from a mathematical point of view, and strove to constrain within the simplest mathematical expressions such complex phenomena as the expansions of liquids, the force of steam at various temperatures, and the relations of the gases to water. The only key to this intellectual inconsistency I can find, was his eminently self-reliant nature and a certain unbendingness of will, near of kin to obstinacy.

I will thank you for any one of the enclosed letters that you may not care to preserve, as an autograph.

Yours very faithfully,
W. C. Henry [1]

The judgment of this letter, coming as it does from a man who was also a pupil of Dalton's and the son of one of his closest friends, cannot be lightly set aside. Yet the letter does reveal its author's impatience with his chosen subject. It also shows a certain failure of sympathy, a failure common to all Dalton's Victorian biographers. Because his greatest intellectual contribution was in the field of chemical theory, W. C. Henry wished

1. Royal Institution, Davy Papers (hereafter referred to as RIDP), no. 107. John Davy had published his *Memoirs of the Life of Sir Humphry Davy* in 1836, in order to "correct" the picture given in J. A. Paris's 1831 *Life of Sir Humphry Davy.*

to paint Dalton, like Davy, as a great chemist and public figure. Henry was correspondingly disappointed by his failure to fill this role, and found Dalton's early life distressingly uneventful and his old age tedious. The failure to exploit and extend the chemical atomic theory seemed lamentable, and his later chemical work worthy only of discreet burial. Blinded by the dazzle of Davy, Henry failed to see the rich significance of Dalton's very different career. The slipshod volume he reluctantly and hurriedly produced concealed rather than displayed the nature and meaning of provincial science. Later biographers inevitably took their cue from Henry.

Despite the succession of books and articles on his life, it is a surprising fact that only seventy-three letters by Dalton have so far been utilized. For many of these letters "publication" has meant only the quotation of a particularly striking phrase or paragraph. Given this situation there is great potential value in any manuscript which has survived the ravages of time, neglect, and war. In fact Dalton seems to have been a vigorous correspondent. The manuscripts of at least ninety-eight of his letters are still extant. What they have to say considerably enlarges, clarifies, and modifies the distorted picture developed by his Victorian biographers.

Though the air-raid on Manchester in 1940 resulted in the destruction of a great number of Dalton documents, ten letters by Dalton (as well as a considerable number to him) are still in the possession of the Manchester Literary and Philosophical Society. There are a further ten letters in the Science Museum in London, and seventy-three others are preserved in a variety of libraries and institutions in Britain. In addition there are at least five letters in American archives. The manuscripts of ninety-eight letters are thus available for examination. Portions of twenty-five of these, ranging from an isolated sentence to a complete text, have already been published. Examination of the original manuscripts shows that several of the printed texts have been subjected to unadvertized editing, but the alterations and suppressions are rarely serious. A long extract previously omitted from one of these letters, and complete texts of seven others from which only brief quotations have hitherto been available, are given below.

Much greater interest attaches to the seventy-three letters now discovered for the first time. Twenty-five of these (in the archives of the Dalton family) are from John to his cousin Henry Dalton, over the years 1834–1842. Though not without the occasional remark of far wider interest, they basically concern the family property in Eaglesfield, and difficulties over rents, tenants, and so on.[2] They will not be published here. Of the remaining forty-eight letters, twenty-five are reproduced in full below, and brief details of the locations and contents of another twenty-one are provided. The remaining two are printed in Chapter 6.

It is naturally a question of some interest how far these unpublished letters are representative of Dalton's life and thought. As Table 1 indicates, the seventy-three Dalton letters that have already been published were drawn in roughly equal numbers from all phases of his life. In contrast the seventy-three unpublished letters now available concentrate more heavily on the latest years. This in part reflects the fact that letters

Table 1. *Letters by Dalton*

Period	Previously published in whole or part	Previously unpublished *	Total
Up to 1793	13	5	18
1793–1800	15	3	18
1801–1808	15	6	21
1809–1818	9	3	12
1819–1832	7	14	20
1833–1844	14	40	52

* The two previously unpublished letters of unknown date are excluded.

2. Dalton (Eaglesfield) Mss., Ref. D/Da, County Record Office, Carlisle. In addition to the 25 letters by John Dalton, packet 1 contains a long series by Jonathan and the wills of the two brothers.

relating to the years 1793–1818, the most interesting period of Dalton's life from a scientific point of view, were most likely to be on display in Manchester and hence destroyed in 1940. However, the thirty-nine letters already published from the period 1793–1818 show quite clearly that Dalton was never primarily an enthusiastic chemist, intent on elaborating and promoting a new atomic theory, as his biographers desired and imagined. The rather different picture that the published letters provide is fully confirmed by the newly discovered correspondence. (See Table 2.)

Meteorology was a popular and important area of research in the eighteenth century. That it was also Dalton's first love and lifelong enthusiasm may be seen from the letters reproduced below. The correspondence commences with the twenty-two-year-old teacher establishing an exchange of meteorological data and ends forty-two years later with a query on the aurora borealis. The letters document Dalton's early realization of the importance of exact meteorological records (letter 1), his perse-

Table 2. *Main Subjects of the Letters*

	Number of letters with main subject:		
Period	*Meteorology*	*Chemistry*	*Miscellaneous*
Up to 1793	4	—	9
	4	—	*1*
1793–1800	4	1	10
	2	—	*1*
1801–1808	3	3	9
	1	2	*3*
1809–1818	1	4	4
	—	—	*3*
1819–1832	3	1	3
	1	*1*	*12*
1833–1844	2	2	10
	3	2	*35*

Note: The figures in roman refer to published and those in italics to previously unpublished letters. The two previously unpublished letters of unknown date are excluded.

verance against the difficulties inherent in his situation and homemade apparatus (letters 2 and 8), and his continuing concern with the subject long after his studies had lost their relevance (letters 27 and 28). The wide range of Dalton's scientific interests is also apparent. His early botanical work (letters 5, 6, and 7) reveals a young man desperately eager to learn and better himself, while two letters (12 and 13) written in his first years in Manchester show him engaged in the study of heat and interested in "galvanic experiments." There is little mention of chemistry in these earlier letters, a fact in keeping with Dalton's greater enthusiasm for other fields. Letter 15 marks the divide. It announces the first detailed, systematic exposition of the "chemical atomic theory."

The later letters show Dalton expressing more interest in chemistry, but there is small indication of any deep and sustained desire for chemical controversy and debate. These later letters also reveal a man held in growing public esteem (letters 17, 18, and Davy's letter), yet determined to hold aloof from Metropolitan squabbles (letters 22 and 23). That his scientific work and abilities could both feed on and be turned directly to the technological problems of the day may be seen from letters 19, 26, and 27. The dry, factual, mundane side of Dalton's nature is evident throughout the correspondence, as is his seeming indifference to the larger social and political issues of the period (as example, letter 11). Yet alongside the determination, the ambition, the factual stress, and the cautious, limited outlook that these letters reveal, Dalton's sense of humor and his concern for family and friends are also apparent. And time and again we catch glimpses of that major speculative ability which underlay all his work and resulted in theories to explain subjects as diverse as color-blindness, mixed gases, expansion by heat, chemical combination, and the aurora borealis.

THE LAKE DISTRICT NATURALIST

The following nine letters were addressed to John Dalton's intimate friend and fellow enthusiast for natural knowledge,

Peter Crosthwaite, the keeper of a Keswick museum. They were all written when Dalton was a resident master in the Quaker boarding school in Kendal, and no replies are extant. The letters beautifully capture the amateur but determined world of provincial natural philosophy at this period. They also present a graphic picture of the young devotee of meteorology, already boldly confident that his labors "will have a proper value [placed] on them, at a time when the importance of exact meteorological observations is fully evinced." That Dalton was careful to see his possible benefactors knew his worth is apparent from Elihu Robinson's correspondence. A January 1790 letter of his discusses how "my cousin John Dalton of Kendal, who seems an adept in the science of meteorology, hath favored me with a very curious table setting forth the state of the barometer, thermometer, quantity of rain, number of wet days, etc. for every month last year." [3]

The early letters also display Dalton's botanical work and the heavy factual stress of much of his correspondence. Letter 6 in particular well reveals his industry and determination. The closing part of letter 8 discloses his cautious and prudent approach to the practical problems of life, while letter 9 provides interesting information about the *Meteorological Observations* and illustrates publishing techniques of the period.

LETTER 1 (To Peter Crosthwaite)

Kendal, 2 mo. 21st, 1788

Esteemed Friend,

After waiting for some time with the most eager expectation for my order of glass tubes, I have received them about a week since. I have made those on thy account and they are now getting frames, so I hope thou mayst have them in a week, or a two at most, together with proper directions respecting them.

I received the journal thou did me the favour to send, in due time. I have cursorily compared it with my own, but not with that exactness I intend to do, thro' a multiplicity of engagements that have called my attention. It seems from the compar-

3. Carlisle Public Library, Jackson Collection, ms. 1 F Wil, p. 102.

ison that the general tendency of the weather is the same in the two places with respect to the barometer, thermometer, winds etc., but that the variations are not always equal, and sometimes remarkably different. I shall with pleasure interchange more journals at the equinoxes, solstices, or other convenient times, and I hope our labours in this respect will have a proper value on them, at a time when the importance of exact meteorological observations is fully evinced.

I hope thou wilt have adverted to the piece in the *Cumberland Pacquet* of the 2ᵈ ult. relating to the rain gauge. We take our water up at 10 at night, and prefer weighing it to measuring, in point of exactness.

Which is all at present from thy sincere friend,

John Dalton.[4]

LETTER 2 (To Peter Crosthwaite)

Kendal, 6 mo. 21st, 1788

Esteemed Friend,

Enclosed is a copy of my journal for the last half year. The substance of it needs no further explanation, but I have lately added a fresh column relative to the tides of the air. These will happen about the same time each day as the tides of the ocean, that is, about 3 hours after the moon has crossed the meridian. I get the moon's southing each day from the *Gentleman's Diary,* and adding 3 hours thereto gives the time of high air (if I may be allowed to call it so), and then dividing the times for any two days gives the time of the intermediate tide. These I set down each day to a quarter of an hour (rejecting odd minutes) in a separate column. What gave rise to this was a supposition that these tides may possibly give birth to some of the more minute changes in the weather, or that they may have some influence on the aurora borealis (a phenomenon which

4. Ms. at the Manchester Literary and Philosophical Society (hereafter referred to as MLPS). The letter is addressed to "Peter Crosthwaite, At the Museum, Keswick." The present Fitz Park Museum in Keswick is the indirect descendant of the museum that Crosthwaite began.

has baffled the sagacity of the last and present age to account for in a satisfactory manner).

The times of the 4 quarters of the moon are also set down together with the times when the moon is in perigee and apogee, or nearest to, and farthest from the earth, in each of its revolutions (as the tides are higher the nearer the moon is to the earth, other circumstances being the same). Since this commenced I have been more particular to the time of the day when any change occurred.

Should have been glad to have embraced this opportunity to send a thermometer, but am totally disappointed. The glass men either despair of pleasing me, or are unwilling to trouble themselves with such trifling matters. The tradesman in this town I employed has received his order in full, but there is no mention made of mine. However I intend to apply somewhere else. The spirit thermometer, which I suppose thou hast yet, might serve thy purpose if it had a Fahrenheit's scale, for 6 or perhaps 12 months without much error. A scale from 0 to 100 might be had by determining any two distant degrees by means of water of different degrees of heat and the other thermometer. The principal objection is the too large bulb.

From what thou hast mentioned of the barometer, I think it is now as high as it can be got, and very near the truth. Thy brother's must be 1 or 2 sixteenths too high for your elevation, I think; and this may arise from 2 causes, either an adulteration of the silver or a wrong measurement from the basin; or perhaps both together.

The real difference in height of our barometers will be found best by comparing the monthly means of the same (which in my journal I put down in inches and decimals at the end of each month) and I suspect that this difference will give a greater difference of elevation of the two places than otherwise we make it. My barometer will be about 20 yards above the sea and if thine be 55, the difference 35 will scarce give $^2/_{16}$ of the barometer. And yet there is great reason to believe thy barometer is as true as mine since I filled it afresh. This leads me to mention a late circumstance. A friend of mine from Cumberland being here mentioned his having seen (he thinks in manuscript at the end of Dr Johnson's *Tour of the Hebrides*) that Skiddow was 1148 yards above the sea and that Grassmere Top was 1145 yards above the sea. Upon this I told him that Donald had made Skiddow 1090 yards above the sea, and that it was supposed the foot of Bassenthwaite was about 40 yards above it. But with this last supposition he said he could not coincide, for it only supposed the river about 4 yds fall for 1 mile, which he was persuaded was much too little; and alleged that he knew several mills upon it where the dam was ½ or 2 yds above the river below, and the dead water in the dam was only two or three hundred yards. Add to this that the mills are generally built on a part of the river where is the least fall: also that he knew the river in general to have a pretty rapid stream. Now from these considerations it would seem that the foot of Bassenthwaite should be set at above 40 yards above the sea. So that it will not appear surprising if our barometers should differ more than $\frac{2}{16}$th.

Please to give me a word relative to the situation of thy thermometer. Mine hangs out in the open air in the garden this fair weather at morn and night, but is under cover at noon and is often I believe too hot, for it is to the south and the roof heated by the sun in clear days. Different situations make sensible variations in them. J. Gough and I mostly agree at morn and night, but the noon observations differ, especially in clear days, sometimes 5 or 6 degrees. However our monthly means come mostly within one or two degrees and often are not one different.

I do not think thou wilt lose anything sensible from thy bottle by evaporation, but can perhaps speak more decisively on this head hereafter, being at present partly engaged on experiments of this nature.

It appears from the public papers, that you have had a respectable number of visitors to the lakes this year already—I hope their curiosity would be no less gratified by a sight of a museum than by the beauties of nature in your vicinity.

If business have hindered thee from completing thy copy, do not hurry on our account.

With best respects, thy friend,

John Dalton.[5]

LETTER 3 (To Peter Crosthwaite?)

Kendal, 6 mo. 26th, 1789

Esteemed Friend,

As John Gough does not seem inclined to part with the antiquity I mentioned, [I] should be glad to know whether a drawing of it or a model would be acceptable to thee, along with the best account that we can give of it.

I think if thou should draw out an account of the quantity of rain thou hast had each month and place; the rain at Kendal along with it; also an account of the height of the clouds, so many observations below 100 yards, so many between 100 and 200 etc., and so many above the top of Skiddow; then if this were placed in some conspicuous part of the museum, it might be a very agreeable sight to those who have a curiosity this way.

Thankful for the favours received, I have the satisfaction to inform thee that the company I had the honour of attending to the museum, were in the highest degree satisfied therewith.

Thy sincere friend,

John Dalton.[6]

LETTER 4 (To Peter Crosthwaite?)

Kendal, 1 mo. 1st, 1790

Esteemed Friend,

Herewith I have sent my journal up to the present year, instead of the shortest day. The reason was because I generally

5. Science Museum, London (hereafter referred to as SML), Ms. no. 1954–353. Addressed to "Peter Crosthwaite, At the Museum, Keswick." A brief excerpt appears in W. C. Henry, *Memoirs of the Life and Scientific Researches of John Dalton* (1854), pp. 18–19. Extracts from several of the letters that follow appear in one or more of the Dalton biographies. In each case a reference to the longest quotation is included. The biographies cited also give more information on the minor figures mentioned in the letters.

6. Ms. at the Wellcome Historical Medical Library, London (hereafter referred to as WHML). No address, but presumably to Peter Crosthwaite.

make a kind of synopsis or epitome of the journal at the end of the year, in order to exhibit at one view the means, extremes etc., of each month; and if it be convenient would have thine up to the same time, without such calculation except thou have made it already; because it will give thee too much trouble. Should have sent this with my brother, who is now in Cumberland, but I believe he will not pass thro' your neighbourhood. There is a surprising difference between the mean of thermometer for December this and last, and also the rain, which has been prodigious lately as will be seen, tho' the frost seems now coming. Notwithstanding the heavy rains we have had no remarkable floods.

My best respects to thyself and family,

John Dalton.[7]

LETTER 5 (To Peter Crosthwaite?)

Kendal, 7 mo. 20th, 1790.

Respected Friend,

I wrote thee a few weeks since by my friend Saul of Cockermouth relative to the *Gentleman's Magazine,* since which I have got the number with the drawing and account of the stone. Also have copied the animadversions thereon from a subsequent number, but J. Gough's reply is not yet published and he has lost or mislaid the copy of it, so that I have only sent the magazine and must wait a little before I can get the manuscript accounts complete. My journal is continued to the beginning of present month. I had above 1.5 rain from 9 last night to 6 this morning. The hay harvest is very broken hitherto, as I suppose it to be with you.

I may inform thee I am at present pursuing the pleasing study of botany. Please to inform me of the name of the plant you had growing in the museum suspended by a string about a year ago. The common stonecrop will do the same in degree, but it loses its weight.

7. Ms. in Liverpool University Library. No address, but presumably to Peter Crosthwaite.

I have sent herewith two or three trifling curiosities of natural history. They may perhaps be deemed puerile, but nothing that enjoys animal life or that vegetates is beneath the dignity of a naturalist to examine. The explanations of the different articles are enclosed. There is a white butterfly and its case or shell, a mottled one and its shell, flesh flies and their small shells and Ichneuemon flies and their silky shells.

I am thine respectfully,
John Dalton.[8]

LETTER 6 (To Peter Crosthwaite)

Kendal, 3 mo. 26th, 1791

Respected Friend,

Having never been so fortunate when at Keswick as to have time sufficient to attend to the vast variety of particulars, I am quite unacquainted with the specimens of your plants and do not know in what manner you have preserved them when dry for the inspection of the curious. But I have myself during last summer dried and pressed a good many and pasted them down to sheets of white paper. I find they look very pretty and attract the attention of all, both learned and unlearned. This has induced me to think that a tolerable collection of them treated in this manner would be a very proper object in the museum, and if I should pursue a similar plan the ensuing summer I could without much additional trouble collect and dry a number of specimens.

I would propose to do it in the following manner—first to get a folio book of good strong writing paper containing 2, 3 or 4 quires, and to paste the dried and pressed plant to one side of each leaf, writing at the same time the Linnaean name and English name on the opposite side, and then to have an alphabetical index to the names referring to the pages.

I cannot say what kind of a recompence would be equivalent to such a task, but think I could engage to fill a book of 2 quires for half a guinea. Whether the acquisition of such a set

8. WHML. No address, but presumably to Peter Crosthwaite.

of plants would be worth the expense to thee I cannot pretend to judge, but if thou should judge so, please to inform me, whether to aim at a general collection of all the plants (growing spontaneously) within my reach, or only such as are more rare, or more pleasing to the eye, etc. But, if such a book of plants be not likely to answer for the expense, this letter need not be taken any notice of.

I am etc.,
John Dalton.[9]

LETTER 7 (To Peter Crosthwaite?)

Kendal, 10 mo. 4th. 1791

Respected Friend,

I have at length completed the book of plants and made an index both to the Linnaean and English names.

I have not covered them with gum copal as desired because I think they will last long enough without it, if kept dry. If they start up much, put in a little paste or dissolve gum tragacanth and press them down with a fold of blotting paper over them.

I was solicitous to pick up the more rare plants, but could not get a collection of them in one season. Have therefore opened a common quire book in which I intend to put such plants whenever I may obtain them. Notwithstanding this, several of the plants are rare here and much more so in other parts of the kingdom, that I am not without hopes that many of the adepts in the science will find something new to them in the collection.

I am not so confident of my abilities as to maintain that I have given no plant a wrong name, but I believe the skilful botanist will find very few, if any, miscalled.

The book cost me 3s. .6d at the stationers.

I am etc.
John Dalton.[10]

9. Ms. at the Historical Society of Pennsylvania, Philadelphia (hereafter referred to as HSP). Addressed to "Peter Crosthwaite, At the Museum, Keswick." Excerpt in Henry, *Memoirs of Dalton*, p. 13.

10. WHML. No address, but presumably to Peter Crosthwaite. Excerpt in Henry, *ibid.*, pp. 13–14. The "book of plants" that Dalton made for Crosthwaite's museum

LETTER 8 (To Peter Crosthwaite?)

Kendal, 1st mo. 11th, 1793

Respected Friend,

I have sent the journal and a thermometer herewith. I mean it to pay thee for the trouble I have given thee in making observations etc. If it should be broken, send the frame and tube back. Thou may try the accuracy of the thermometer any day, by begging a pound or two of ice, breaking it into small pieces, and mixing with a quantity of water, and they will, if true, stand at the freezing point. Snow will do also.

Thou should make a memorandum in the journal how far the *new* barometer scale is distant from the *old* one, at the mark 31 inches. I find that at the beginning of '90 thou hast poured a quantity of silver into the basin to raise the barometer about 2 sixteenths, instead of altering the scale. I reasoned upon it thus I suppose, that as the barometer was wrong 4 sixteenths at 28, it would be wrong 2 sixteenths at 29½, and that therefore if it were raised 2 sixteenths, the errors on one side would balance those on the other. This reasoning is not bad. However, putting on a narrow slip of paper for a new scale is preferable. I consider both our barometers as inaccurate with respect to the distance of the *basins and scales,* but this is of little importance provided they be true in other respects. This only serves to show the relative heights of the places to the sea, which we can come at better by other means. I have therefore in thy calculations on thy barometer taken it for granted that the distance between the surface of the basin and the mark 31 of the old scale, *for the last 3 years,* is true. This being admitted, the *true* method of correcting for the short scale is easy and very readily done as follows: Find the monthly mean of scale. Deduct it from 31. Divide the remainder by 12. The quotient added to the before found mean gives the correct mean. Thus the mean for January '90 by the journal is 29.788; the correct mean is 29.889; and the like for any *particular* observation. And for the two former years I make the further *constant addition* of 2 sixteenths, or rather .12 decimals.

I would not have thee labour too much with Skiddow considering the season of the year. It is not a matter of the greatest importance to know its height, and with respect to the other mountains I only meant to have their altitudes in round numbers, as seen from a place in the vale, to about 8 Points of the Compass.

I noted thy paragraph in the *Cumberland Pacquet*. We have just about as much rain here as last year, and snow on the night of the 4th inst. Thou would do well to examine whether thy gauge be *truly level*. J. Gough's and mine were both thrown aside a little last month by the frost or something, mine to the leeward and his to the windward. The consequence was that he beat me surprisingly on windy days.

I cannot get my calabash into this box. It is but a fractured one also. I may probably meet with some opportunity of sending it. J. Gough heard of that fish when here, and wished to examine it, but for some reason or other missed. It is doubtless worth a place in the museum.

If the journal come in a week or ten days there will be no fault.

I must now add a word respecting Walker:

J. Gough and I are both of opinion, that if the paper be sent up under a *borrowed name* it will not be inserted; but probably it may if with thy own name; and that it should be sent nearly as it is, without much addition or alteration. If thou should make additions respecting the character of the museum, etc. it would look like ostentation, and if it were under a fictitious name, most people would judge thee to be the author, or at least the instigator of it. Besides there is little consistency in uniting a piece of criticism with anything of the nature of an advertisement.

Upon the whole therefore we do not wish to press thee any one way, but to leave it to thy own judgment. Yet we think it will be most prudent to send it in thy *own name,* and nearly as it is drawn up, or else to suppress it entirely. As to the "paper war" we think it out of the question. He is so obviously wrong that he has no ground to stand upon. If we fear anything, it is, that he will be so malicious as to seek for a handle to call thee to account *another way.* This indeed may be avoided by using a fictitious name but then the risk falls upon the publisher, and it is *great odds* he refuses its insertion.

I am thine respectfully,

John Dalton.[11]

LETTER 9 (To Peter Crosthwaite)

Kendal, 4 mo. 18th, 1793

Respected Friend,

I send thee herewith a parcel of my advertisements which thou mayst order as may best suit—also an antique shilling, being one of Elizabeth's, procured by my friend J. Gough. Its cost was one shilling, which may be put to account.

It will be unnecessary to remark my very high satisfaction with thy observations on the *aurora.* I think no one could have done better. I should wish to know whether the observation of the altitude was repeated or only taken once. Upon reviewing my observations I find the altitude here was $53°$; thine was $48°$; the difference $5°$ gives the height about 150 miles!

I think the true altitude *here* could not be $2°$ over or under; probably there the altitude would be within $2°$ of $48°$ also. The height of this arc must therefore be very great and much higher than the atmosphere has usually been supposed. I should like to have at some opportunity the notes thou hast made upon the *other* aurora this winter, and then I think thou may desist from so *watchful* and *particular* care of these phenomena, as we shall hardly have another opportunity so fine as that above, of determining their height, and the busy season with you is coming on.

11. SML. Ms. no. 1954–354. No address, but presumably to Peter Crosthwaite. Excerpt in Henry, *ibid.,* p. 13.

I mean to get W. Pennington to print the work and to put it to press shortly, or as soon as 100 or 150 copies are spoke for, which I expect will not be long. I spoke to him to mention the *museum* etc. in the new edition of the *Guide,* but he seemed not very free to do it. I shall endeavour to make amends in mine, and as I expect my *Essays* will merit the attention of the curious, they may possibly circulate pretty rapidly.

I make the latitude of Kendal 54°17' and suppose that of Keswick will be about 54.30.

Thou hast not got Phipp's (Mulgrave) *Voyage to the North?* He finds the dip in the needle in different places: I want to know it.

I am etc.,

John Dalton.[12]

THE MANCHESTER PROFESSOR

It was in the summer of 1793 that Dalton left Kendal for Manchester, where he was to remain for the rest of his life (almost fifty-one years). Letter 10 gives a glimpse of him on one of the return visits that he made to the Lake District nearly every year. Letter 11 is part of a very long, informative account of a trip to Wales, Oxford, and London that Dalton made in 1798. About two-thirds of this letter has already been published, but the section below, previously omitted, is of interest on two counts. His almost pained inclusion of the information that "many of the poor preferred begging and pining in want and obscurity" to entering the workhouse illustrates well his lack of concern with social issues. Also, the Victorian myth of Dalton's own nearness to poverty is hard to sustain. He already enjoyed a modest security even before the move to Manchester. As the list of those he visited on his tour shows, he mixed easily in circles of some wealth. Letter 12 indicates Dalton's growing inter-

12. HSP. Addressed to "Peter Crosthwaite, Museum, Keswick." Excerpt in Henry, *ibid.,* p. 19. See also J. Dalton, *Meteorological Observations and Essays,* 2nd ed. (Manchester, 1834), p. vii.

est in the properties of water, that commodity so freely available to the meteorologist and scientific inquirer in both the Lake District and Manchester. The contact with Priestley's son is of interest, and the comment on America not without a certain unconscious humor for us today.

LETTER 10

Kendal, 8th mo. 27th, 1794

Respected Friend Thomas Wilkinson,

Agreeably to thy request I have sent thee the result of my observations on the heights of places above the sea. I was very well pleased my route had been directed by Hawswater and Longsledale. The water was the most peaceful I ever saw, and the diversity of the scenery in the vale afterwards had a fine effect. I arrived at Kendal about 8 in the evening.

I remain thy assured friend,

John Dalton.[13]

Account of the heights of places above the sea, determined by the barometer in 7th and 8th months, 1794.

Names of places	Height above the sea in yards
Winardermere lake	36
Crook	120
Esthwaite lake	66
Langdale chapel stile	76
Dunmail raise gap	276
Leathes lake	206
Whinlater (top of the road)	346
Keswick	81
Eaglesfield	151
Carlisle	15

13. WHML. No address. Some of the heights given, together with others supplied by Dalton, appear in John Robinson, *A Guide to the Lakes in Cumberland, Westmorland and Lancashire*, 1819, 323–324. On Thomas Wilkinson, see also ch. 2, n. 15 above.

Names of places	Height above the sea in yards
Siotby	35
Dalston	45
Coldbeck (town)	183
Wurnel fell (turnpike gate)	338
Greenrigge	320
Crummock water	91
Grasmere hill	953
Smithy, foot of Carrock	238
Carrock, west pike	744
east pike	713
Mossdale	266
Bowscale tarn	540
Penrith	134
Emont bridge	126
Penrith beacon	340
Yanwath	156
Tirril	196
Winder	366
Hawswater	238
Top of Goatscar (the road over it)	663
Kendal	46

Most of the following letter has already been published. The manuscript is now in poor condition. The section not previously published runs as follows:

LETTER 11 (To Elihu Robinson)

Manchester, 1st mo. 27th, 1798

. . . we had each about 8 or 10 cups of coffee.

I could scarcely fail to mention our rapturous enjoyment of the scenery about Hawkston, the seat of Sir Richard Hill. With respect to the house of industry at Shrewsbury—we had an introduction to a Mr Mason, a principal merchant of the city, who was one of the Patrons of the institution and who was so obliging as to accompany us and give us every information. An account of it has been printed by one concerned, so that we did not take notes. It seemed very clean and neat; the provisions good; the people cheerful and tidy; and a general activity pervaded every department. I think any person is entitled to partake of its benefits who complies with the rules, and is at liberty to leave it in like manner. Under all these advantages we were informed that many of the poor preferred begging and pining in want and obscurity, to taking up their residence here, where rules and ordinances were to be attended to, and where industry was the order of the day. Even complaints of mismanagement were urged:—on our descending the hill we met an infirm old woman. Our guide asked her if she belonged to the house? Yes. Was she content in her situation? No. What was amiss? The apothecary did not allow her what was proper for her asthmatic complaint. Why, how could that be, as the apothecary was not interested in the case? She did not know, but so it was. Do you know that I am of the Committee? Yes, Sir, I do. Observe then, I shall expect and require of you to bring this charge before the Board on Monday next. Have you any complaint in any other respect? None.

At Kitley we were introduced to Joseph Reynolds, Richard's son at whose house we stayed a day, except the time taken up in viewing the works. A pupil of mine, an old acquaintance, walked over with us to Coalbrookdale. William Rathbone gave us an introduction to his father Richard Reynolds, but as it happened it was unnecessary for both himself and wife were there, and a young Norwegian gentleman under his care who had just left our Academy. Richard Reynolds and wife were very well, and shewed us every attention. Their company and that of their daughter Rathbone (one of the most amiable of her sex) made the evening very pleasant, for William R. was gone to Ketley. We saw Richard Dearman, who was well, and invited us to call, but we had not time. In the morn Richard Reynolds procured a man to show us the Ironworks. This done, it was noon on *seventh* day. We held a consultation whether to stay next morning's meeting or proceed to some other, when it appeared practicable to reach Stourbridge. The young Norwegian joined us to Birmingham. We took an early dinner, walked down to survey the Iron Bridge, where we ordered a chaise, and were presently at Bridgnorth whence we walked to Enville that night, 10 miles. Next morn we had 5 miles to Stourbridge, and all three attended the meeting. After, went to Hagley to dine; traversed Hagley park and the Leasower that afternoon and reached Birmingham by 10 at night. Here we experienced the friendly assistance of Samuel Lloyd and another in introducing us to the manufactories. At Worcester I was acquainted with friend Newman's family and others who were very obliging to us. We had a very fine day for our visit to Blenheim house. At Oxford we had a line to one of the Fellows . . .[14]

LETTER 12 (To Jonathan Dalton)

Manchester, 3 mo. 28th, 1799

Dear Brother,

Nothing particular has occurred since my last to inform thee of. We had snow an inch deep on the ground on the 16th, and on the 26th at 4 p.m. we had a heavy hail shower. I gathered near a peck of hailstones in a small compass for certain experiments.

Have lately been making some curious experiments on the congelation of water in certain circumstances. Have cooled it down to $5°$ or $6°$ without freezing, by putting it into a thermometer tube. I find it almost impracticable to freeze it in such circumstances above $15°$ or $20°$. When it does freeze it is instantaneous, and the liquor shoots up the tube as if ejected

14. Ms. at the Library of the Society of Friends, London (hereafter referred to as LSF). For the previously published sections of this letter to Elihu Robinson, see Henry Lonsdale, *John Dalton*, The Worthies of Cumberland, no. 5 (1874), 47–150. For the people mentioned in this letter, see A. Raistrick, *Quakers in Science and Industry* (1950). Dalton's description of his tour should be compared with a similar one by Thomas Young in 1795. See G. Peacock, *Life of Thomas Young* (1855), pp. 74–75.

by a syringe and often bursts the bulb with a report. The degree of greatest condensation in water is however at 42°, that temperature giving the lowest point in the scale of a water thermometer. The most remarkable fact however, and one which has never that I know of been ascertained before, is that water expands below 42° exactly as it does above, namely according to the number of degrees. Thus water of 32° is of equal density with water of 52°, and water of 6° equal to water of 78° etc, but the moment it freezes its dimensions are increased.

On first day last I dined in the country at a gentleman's where was a large party, amongst others Dr. Priestley's son just arrived from America. He gives a moderately favourable account of America.

I remain etc.,

John Dalton.[15]

THE PERIOD OF THE ATOMIC THEORY

The years from 1801 to 1808 are those in which Dalton formulated, propounded, and published his views on chemical combination. They are therefore of the utmost interest. However, in contrast with what one might infer from a casual reading, the opening paragraph of letter 13 is not concerned with chemistry at all. Instead the *"one* subject" that had engaged Dalton for five months must have been his *Elements of English Grammar* (Manchester, 1801). The letter provides a good illustration of his industrious and ambitious nature. The pressure on his time, his sense of humor, and his awareness of the latest fields of scientific interest are all vividly conveyed. In similar vein, letter 14 (see Figure 8) shows how seriously yet he took his scientific duties. As secretary he was zealous to advance the interests of the Manchester Literary and Philosophical Society,

15. Ms. at the National Library of Scotland. Addressed to "Jonathan Dalton, Kendal." Excerpt in Lonsdale, *Dalton,* pp. 135–136.

Manchester, Aug. 24 - 1802

Sir,

I am desired by the Literary & Philosophical Society of Manchester to return their thanks to the American Philosophical Society for their very acceptable Presents of the 4th & 5th volumes of their Transactions, both of which have been received; & at the same time to transmit our 4th & 5th vol. of Memoirs, each in two Parts, for their acceptance.

We have now your 2d, 4th & 5 Volumes; what you may have already of ours I cannot learn, but have no doubt the Society will wish to complete them, if in their power, when they know what you want.

This Society will cheerfully accord with the reciprocity of communication.

I remain with respect

Your's sincerely

John Dalton, Sect.

P.S. I have inclosed a Volume of Meteorological Observations & Essays published by me a few years ago, for the Society's acceptance.

8. Dalton as Administrator: A Letter to Philadelphia. From the archives of the American Philosophical Society. (Courtesy of the Society.)

although as scientist he was not afraid to promote his own publications.

Great interest attaches to letter 15, for it was in Edinburgh in April 1807 that Dalton gave the first detailed public account of his ideas on "chemical elements or atoms." The chemist Thomas Thomson was apparently the recipient of this letter, for what appears to be his reply has already been published, and Dalton's lectures certainly were held in his classroom. Thomas Thomson was also a close friend of William Henry. Henry had recently returned to Manchester from Edinburgh and may well have been the "some of my acquaintance" to whom Dalton refers.

Over the years Dalton played an increasingly prominent part in the affairs of the Manchester Literary and Philosophical Society. Letter 16 is typical of many he must have written as its vice-president at the time. Also reproduced below is Davy's communication to him about a polar expedition. The offer of £400 or £500 for an engagement of "probably only three or four months" illustrates the sort of patronage available via the officers of the Royal Society and other favored Metropolitan *savants*. The letter was actually published long ago, but without the postscript which goes some way to explain why Dalton refused the offer (and which also indicates that he was by no means Davy's first choice for the post?).

LETTER 13 (To John Fell)

Manchester, 4 mo. 5th, 1801

Respected Friend,

I received thine of the 28th of 2 mo. Thou wilt easily imagine that my leisure time has lately been almost wholly engaged upon *one* subject. That I have now finished, and am glad of it, as it will give me a little relief, and suffer my attention to be turned to subjects of an experimental nature again. I have herewith sent thy daughter a specimen of my lucubrations for the last 5 months, which I desire her to accept. Whether she will think I had better saved the "midnight oil" for an illumi-

nation at the restoration of peace [16] I know not, but certain it
is that no inconsiderable part of the performance was affected
between the hours of 11 and 1.

I was much pleased with thy detail of the improvement
made in that pleasing and interesting electric experiment, but
should suppose the complex motion would now require a high
charge. However it serves admirably to shew the efficacy of the
electric powers. Two days ago I dined with S. Taylor at his
house in the country. He informed me he had just got a letter
from Cuthbertson acquainting him that two plates were just
come to hand and he wished to know if they were to be fitted
up. S.T. wrote him he intended to be in London shortly and
would call upon him relative to it. Since then he has given up
his intention of going to town, and intends to write him to go
forward with it. S.T. tells me he intends to be married in two
months.

The galvanic experiments appear to me very curious. I have
not had time to think much about them. I think Dr. Herschel's
experiments upon heat rank amongst the most important made
for a century past.[17]

William Henry has just presented me with his *Epitome of
Chemistry*.[18] It seems a very useful manual for one tolerably acquainted with the principles of chemistry.

With best respects to thy wife and daughter,
I remain thy obliged friend,

John Dalton.[19]

LETTER 14 (To John Redman Coxe)
Manchester, Aug. 24, 1802
Sir,

I am desired by the Literary and Philosophical Society of
Manchester to return their thanks to the American Philosophi-

16. The short-lived "peace of Amiens."
17. See the papers by William Herschel in *Philosophical Transactions of the Royal Society of London* 90 (1800), 255–283 ff.
18. Henry's 1801 textbook enjoyed wide popularity and expanded through many editions.
19. SML. Ms. no. 1954–355. Addressed to "John Fell, Ulverstone."

cal Society for their very acceptable presents of the 4th and 5th volumes of their *Transactions,* both of which have been received, and at the same time to transmit our 4th and 5th volumes of *Memoirs,* each in two parts, for their acceptance.

We have now your 2nd, 4th and 5th volumes. What you may have already of ours I cannot learn, but have no doubt the Society will wish to complete them, if in their power, when they know what you want.

This Society will cheerfully accord with the reciprocity of communication.

I remain with respect,

Yours sincerely,

John Dalton, Secretary.[20]

P.S. Have enclosed a volume of *Meteorological Observations and Essays* published by me a few years ago, for the Society's acceptance.

LETTER 15 (To Thomas Thomson?)

Manchester, March 2nd, 1807

Respected Friend,

It having been suggested to me by some of my acquaintance, that an explication of my late experimental enquiries on the subjects of *heat, elastic fluids, and chemical elements or atoms* with their various combinations, would not be unacceptable at Edinburgh, I have been induced to propose, provided it meet with your countenance, to spend 2 or 3 weeks in Edinburgh, and to deliver a short course of 4 or 5 lectures, principally on the subjects above mentioned, containing an account of my latest results, some of which have not yet been published or disclosed in any way, and which I conceive of considerable importance. The subscription I would propose to be half a guinea.

I shall be glad to have your opinion on the subject by a line in the course of a few days, together with any suggestion which

---

20. Ms. at the American Philosophical Society Library, Philadelphia. Addressed to "John Redman Coxe, M.D., Secretary to the American Philosophical Society, Philadelphia."

may occur to you respecting the execution of the design, if deemed plausible.

In the mean time I remain,

Your assured friend,

J. Dalton.[21]

P.S. I should probably be in Edinburgh in the course of 2 or 3 weeks from this time.

LETTER 16 (To Messrs Cadell and Davies, printers?)

Manchester, May 1st, 1810

Respected Friends,

I received your letter of the 9th ult. which appears to me as well as to other members of the Society to have been written under an erroneous impression, or we rest under one. Dr Hull was the Corresponding Secretary at the time of our last publication, when it was resolved by the Committee to offer the *Memoirs* to some respectable bookseller who would publish them at his own risk and expense, with certain other conditions. If we are not under a misapprehension you declined this offer. Mr Bickerstaff was next applied to and he accepted the terms. No steps have been taken nor wish signified to transfer the sale of the preceding volumes from you to him, except that it was agreed he should be supplied with copies if called for.

I have written to Mr Bickerstaff and doubt not he will take your remaining copies of the 4th and 5th volumes. In the mean time if you will be so good as to send your account, I will lay it before the Committee in order to receive directions for settling the same.

I remain yours,

Respectfully,

J. Dalton.[22]

21. WHML. No address, but presumably to Thomas Thomson. His reply is printed in H. E. Roscoe and A. Harden's *New View of the Origins of Dalton's Atomic Theory* (1896), pp. 141–142.

22. Ms. at Carlisle Public Library. No address, but presumably to Messrs Cadell and Davies, printers. See F. Nicholson, "The Literary and Philosophical Society 1781–1851," *Manchester Memoirs 68* (1924), no. 9.

Davy's letter to Dalton is as follows:

23 Grosvenor Street,
February 12, 1818

My Dear Sir

You have probably heard of the expedition which is preparing for investigating the polar regions. The Royal Society, charged by the Admiralty with the scientific arrangements of this voyage, is very desirous of making the most of so interesting an opportunity of investigating many important objects relating to meteorology and the theory of the earth.

They have obtained from the Admiralty the power of recommending a natural philosopher to go on this expedition and it has occurred to me that if you find your engagements and your health such as to enable you to undertake the enterprise no one will be so well qualified as yourself.

Probably £400 or £500 a year will be allowed during the voyage. It may last from one to two years but more probably only three or four months. In all events it is believed that the whole year's salary will be allowed.

This plan may not in any way fall in with your views. At all events I am sure you will not be displeased with me for enquiring if such a proposition will be acceptable to you and impute this letter to the high respect I have for your talents and achievements and the desire that they may be brought into activity and extended and rewarded as they ought to be.

I am my dear sir,
Very sincerely yours,
H. Davy.[23]

The favour of an early answer is required, as the expedition will certainly sail before the 10th of March.

THE YEARS OF FAME

By the 1820's the significance for chemistry of relative particle weight studies was widely recognized, and Dalton received a

23. RIDP. No. 105. Excerpt in W. C. Henry, *Memoirs of Dalton*, pp. 161–162.

variety of public honors. His intention to visit "the chemical people" at Paris is revealed in Letter 16a, while Letter 17 indicates a different type of invitation. Letter 18 shows another aspect of his fame. However, letter 20 indicates that his zeal for the advancement of science was not allowed to override a very lively sense of his own self-interest. Letters 19 and 21 refer to volume 2, part 1 of the *New System,* which belatedly appeared in 1827. Dalton's lack of enthusiasm for "such unprofitable business" is apparent. Finally in two letters of 1830 to Charles Babbage, we see how little Dalton cared for the internecine warfare of the Metropolitan *savants.* One would not easily realize from these letters that Babbage was in the midst of a bitter struggle to reform the Royal Society, or that his *Decline of Science* made some highly complimentary remarks about Dalton.

LETTER 16a (To Benjamin Dockray?)

Manchester, 6 mo. 10th, 1822.

Dear Friend,

I received thy favour this morning and feel much obliged to thee for the offer of thy company, which could not but be highly acceptable to me were I to pay a visit to Paris, and indeed it operates as a stimulus to pay that visit.

W. Crewdson Junior's company would be an additional pleasure as far as I am concerned.

If our times and views should meet I should like to be one of the party. I could not very well be ready to leave here in less than a week or ten days after receiving thy reply; I should not wish to spend more than a day or two in London either going or returning; If I left this place two weeks hence it would suit me the better. My views are to go to Paris by any tolerably direct route; to spend a week or two in it and the environs; to visit a few of the chemical people who might be at home etc.— to see the curiosities etc. etc.—and then to return by some variation of the route either by Havre or circuitously by Brussels, Ostend, through Norfolk home again, so as to be absent about a month.

My times and views must of course be understood to bend as far as convenient to those of the party, but I should not feel comfortable to lose thy company on the return, if thy visit would require a longer or shorter time than the one I propose, unless W. Crewdson or some other acquaintance could be met with, in some measure to supply thy place as travelling companion.

Having given thee the particulars of my views, I shall wait a few days for thy reply, before I contemplate any other summer excursion.

I remain thy assured friend,

John Dalton.[23a]

LETTER 17 (To James Williamson)

Manchester, November 8th, 1823

Respected Friend,

On looking over your favour of the 23rd October I am almost ashamed at not having replied to it more early, but I have been suffering great part of the time from a severe cold, an affection to which I am subject occasionally, during the winter season more particularly, and besides have been more than ordinarily busy on account of the commencement of the Society's meetings, etc.

I have no doubt I should feel gratified with the opportunity of delivering a few lectures to a class of such respectability as might be expected in Leeds, and under the patronage of the Philosophical Society, if the subjects were such as I am most familiar with—for example, chemical principles, select principles of mechanics or meteorology, etc. I was not aware till yesterday that your letter mentions *"before* Christmas," and am in doubt whether I have not delayed till it may be too late. I had taken up the idea that it was *after* Christmas.

You have now my sentiments on the proposition. If it be too

23a. Copy in Manchester Central Library. Local History sec. Biographical file. No address, but presumably to Benjamin Dockray, who accompanied Dalton to Paris. For details of the visit, see Henry, *Memoirs of Dalton,* pp. 164–168.

late to meet the Society's views, be mine the fault. Perhaps another opportunity may occur. As for pecuniary remuneration, I should expect no insurmountable objections could arise on that score.

I have mislaid, or rather I think lent your former letters to a meteorological friend, which prevents any remark at present.

I remain yours truly,

John Dalton.[24]

LETTER 18 (To John Fletcher)

Cockermouth, 7 mo. 18th, 1824

Respected Friend John Fletcher,

Some years ago a portrait painter of eminence in Manchester offered to paint my likeness, provided it should be hung up in the Room of the Literary and Philosophical Society. Some of the members were deputed to wait on me to solicit I would sit for the purpose. I consented on the understanding that the Society should be at no *expense* on that account. The likeness being generally deemed a good one, some time after they began to talk of an engraving on a reduced scale. I could not help but hear of such a design, and being aware it must be attended with great expenses, I did all I could to discourage it under a persuasion that whoever undertook it would be a loser, and plainly signified that no pecuniary assistance was to be expected from me. However it was done, in what manner I know not. The undertaker presented me with a copy, which I gave to my brother, on which I thought I could hardly refuse to take a copy or two for my distant friends. I immediately thought of John Fletcher and Ponsonby Harris as claiming a preference on several accounts.

When I consider how much I owe to thy instruction, and how inadequate a remuneration was given, I feel pleasure in being able to make that sort of recompence which at this dis-

24. SML. Ms. no. 1954–356. Addressed to "James Williamson, M.D., Park Square, Leeds." Dalton gave six lectures on mechanics and meteorology. He was also made an honorary member of the Leeds "Phil and Lit." See E. Kitson Clark, *History of the Leeds Philosophical and Literary Society* (Leeds, Jowett and Sowry, 1924), pp. 34–35.

tance of time, and under existing circumstances, I hope thou wilt have no objection to receive.

I remain thy assured friend,

John Dalton.[25]

LETTER 19 (To John Sharpe)

Manchester, November 20th, 1824

Esteemed Friend,

It afforded me great pleasure to receive your kind remembrance of the Literary and Philosophical Society, as well as of myself, and particularly so to learn of your improving health. I had heard of your removal into the neighbourhood of London by Mr Johns' family, who have spent two midsummer holidays at Leamington, chiefly on account of Miss Johns' health. The first summer I desired Mrs Johns, if she met you anywhere in company, to give my best respects. She had not the opportunity at that time. I requested the same at the last season. On their return Mrs Johns informed me you had left Leamington as above, and that she had some conversation with a lady there who was exceedingly regretting your removal, from her loss of Mrs Sharpe, of whom she spoke in most respectful terms.

In reply to your enquiry, the Society published the 4th volume of *Memoirs* (new series) a few months ago—sold by Mr G. Wilson, Essex Street, Strand, price 12/-. I hope you will find there is not much falling off. In regard to *number* the Society has greatly increased the last 2 or 3 years. I think we are 130 or more members; but as usual the *labouring* ones are not very numerous. (N.B. There is an awkward typographical error in the new volume of *Memoirs,* if not corrected with the pen. The matter of page 514 should be in page 516, and vice versa).

Your paper on steam [26] has been very respectfully quoted in more than one instance lately. M. Clement (of Paris) who was lately here, maintains from his experiments that the heat from

25. Fitz Park Museum, Keswick. Addressed to "John Fletcher, Greysouthen." Fletcher was Dalton's first teacher, half a century before. For the portrait, see Frontispiece.

26. See *Manchester Memoirs* 7 (1813), 1–14.

a given *weight* of steam is the same whether of 8 atmospheres force, or ¼ of an inch of force. I think however that we should have several good authorities for so important a fact.

I have lately been paying attention to the heat and light from burning gases. The heat I find is in proportion to the oxygen consumed, whether the combustible gas is pure or mixed, but the light is not exactly as the oxygen, and is wonderfully diminished by dilution. The best coal gas when diluted with common air, each half, gives no *light* worth anything, but it gives the same *heat* as before.[27]

The 2nd volume of my *Chemistry* is not yet published. I have had the first part of it printed for some years, and it is now only waiting for a finish which I have not yet accomplished, but hope I shall soon. It will afford me great pleasure to send you a copy the very earliest opportunity.

Give me leave to return thanks for your kind invitation. My visits to London are not frequent, and mostly unforeseen, but I shall not forget you when there. Last spring I spent 2 weeks in town on account of the Gas Bills, but was so engaged as to have less time to spare for visiting my acquaintance than I could have wished.

You will have the goodness to present my best respects to Mrs Sharpe; and to accept the same yourself from

Your much obliged friend,
John Dalton.[28]

LETTER 20 (To James Williamson)

Manchester, April 12, 1825

Respected Friend,

In reply to your address of the 8th inst. I must beg leave to

---

27. The previous day the Manchester Gas Company had ordered "that Mr. Dalton have access to the Gasworks at all times . . . and every requisite apparatus for the purpose of experiments." The following year he was once again to give expert testimony before a Parliamentary Committee. See E. Patterson, *John Dalton and the Atomic Theory* (New York 1970), pp. 215–216. For the results of his experimental investigations, see *Manchester Memoirs 9* (1824), 527.

28. WHML. Addressed to "John Sharpe, Esq." Sharpe had been a Manchester attorney.

decline complying with your request. Were I to lend any material part of my apparatus at all, I should not scruple to commence with my friends at Leeds and on such an occasion. But as there are two or three other similar institutions, equally in want of apparatus, and which would have an equal claim upon me, I do not see how I can grant in one case and refuse in another. I know too from experience the danger and delays in carriage, being at this moment inconvenienced from the want of 2 boxes of glass apparatus lately with me at Birmingham, which have been due 10 days and no intelligence of them yet.

Our town's mechanics have a lecture this evening. I believe they are as yet entirely without apparatus. I am glad to hear of the activity of your Philosophical Society.

I remain yours truly,

John Dalton.[29]

LETTER 21 (To William Miller)

Manchester, 11th mo. 20th, 1827

Respected Friend,

I received thine duly and should have answered it sooner, but an unusual press of business since has hitherto prevented. I am greatly obliged to thee for thy care and advice. I approve of thy proposal to leave the whole number of copies with Mac-Lachlan and Stewart, also that they should advertise it once or twice. Perhaps once in a newspaper, and once on the cover of one of the quarterly journals will suffice for a work of this nature. I have subjoined a form for the advertisement to which they can attach the names of any other booksellers, if desireable.

As I am anxious not to trouble thee further unnecessarily upon such unprofitable business, I should wish that when thou

29. E. F. Smith Memorial Collection in the History of Chemistry, University of Pennsylvania (hereafter referred to as EFS). Addressed to "Dr. Williamson, Leeds." Williamson was secretary of the Leeds "Phil. and Lit." Dalton's anxiety over the return of his apparatus, following his lectures at the Birmingham Philosophical Institute, illustrates one problem faced by itinerant lecturers. See also his further letter of 14 April 1825, listed below.

callst again upon Mr Blackwood, if he should not have examined about the old volumes, that thou wouldst desire him to
write me a line as soon as he has made the examination respecting them. In that case MacLachlan and Stewart would probably
refund thee thy expenses and place it to my account, and then
thou needest have no more trouble about the business.

Feeling grateful for thy friendly aid, I remain,

Thy assured friend,
John Dalton.[30]

LETTER 22 (To Charles Babbage)

Manchester, May 15th, 1830
Respected Friend Mr. Babbage,

I received the favour of a copy of your recent publication
through Dr Henry a few days ago, and I feel under great obli-
gation for your kindness. The work gives me much information
(especially as to the Royal Society) which I had not before.
There will be few, I think, who will not agree with you in several of your strictures; though they may differ from you in others. If the work should stimulate the officers and other active
members of the Royal Society to the performance of their duties, it may be of essential service to the promotion of science. I
shall be glad to find that it has that effect.

I remain yours truly,

John Dalton.[31]

LETTER 23 (To Charles Babbage)

Manchester, December 7th, 1830
Respected Friend,

Yours of the 27th ult. came to hand on the 29th. I could not
answer it in time for the elections. I consider Mr Herschel as

30. National Library of Scotland. Addressed to "William Miller, 2 Buccleugh
Place, Edinburgh." The "old volumes" are those of parts 1 and 2 of the *New System of Chemical Philosophy;* the advertisements and new arrangements refer to
"volume 2, part 1" of the work, belatedly published in 1827.

31. British Museum (hereafter referred to as BM), Add. Mss. 37,185, f. 176. Addressed "To Charles Babbage Esq., etc., etc." For his references to Dalton, see

having a profound knowledge in the mathematical and physical sciences in general, and I think that many of the Fellows of the Society who put him in nomination are of great respectability for science. With the little personal acquaintance I have with Mr Herschel and indeed with the characters and writings of the great majority of the Fellows of the Royal Society, it would ill become me to step forward in a prominent point of view to support one person rather than another. If Mr Herschel had been elected to the Chair I should have been highly satisfied, and I think his abilities might be of great use in the Council of the Society. I have seen one or more papers published, in which physical and mathematical acumen were not very conspicuous in the selection.

I remain yours etc.,

John Dalton.[32]

P.S. Not recollecting Mr Herschel's address, I may trouble you if you should see him to give my respectful compliments for his excellent essay on sound.

LATER LIFE

On 31 January 1832 William Henry wrote to John Davy concerning the latter's projected biography of Humphry Davy. Henry's letter contains an interesting paragraph about Dalton, his close friend for more than thirty years: "Mr. Dalton, though falling into years, still continues in tolerable health, tho' accidental ailments now leave more distinct traces upon him than formerly. His mind is still active and vigorous, but he continues too much occupied in teaching mathematics to do much in science. Indeed I suspect he has 'shot his shaft,' like

Charles Babbage, *Reflections on the Decline of Science in England* (1830), pp. 20–21. To serve his own immediate polemical purposes, Babbage here launched the canard that Dalton's talents were languishing, "employed in the drudgery of elementary instruction."

32. BM. Add. Mss. 37,185 f. 370. Addressed to "Charles Babbage Esq., Dorset Street, Manchester Square, London." The most recent account of the power struggles in the Royal Society at this period is A. C. Todd, *Beyond the Blaze. A Biography of Davies Gilbert* (D. Bradford Barton, Truro, 1967), pp. 207–267.

most other men who have lived upwards of 60 years." [33] His preoccupation with pedagogy was not the hindrance to science that Henry supposed, for even in his most creative years Dalton's main activity had been teaching. So suited to him was this style of life that in 1818 he refused an admirer's offer to provide that laboratory and private income which would allow him to "devote himself to science." [34] Rather it seems that all Dalton's enduring scientific work was completed between the ages of twenty-five and fifty-five, in the intervals between the multitude of routine tasks that provided welcome relief from abstract research.

Dalton lived to be seventy-seven. It is clear from his correspondence that he kept up his scientific interests well into his later years. If he made no first-rank research contributions in the 1820's and 1830's, he continued to do serious work and to enjoy a wide acquaintance. Letter 23a provides a reminder of the rich scientific culture of the English provinces in Dalton's lifetime. Letter 29 reveals how he was highly delighted with the Dublin meeting of the British Association for the Advancement of Science, despite the poor reception there given to his ideas on molecular structure. The letters to J. L. Gay-Lussac and to Major Emmett show him still active in research in the early 1830's. A change came in 1837, when he suffered two strokes. From then on Dalton was in poor health, with failing powers and imperfect memory. His 1840 notes to Michael Faraday are those of an old man, stubbornly holding on to his ideas.

LETTER 23a (To John Marshall)

Manchester, September 27th, 1835.

Esteemed Friend,

I hope to be excused for presuming to introduce to your notice and that of your amiable family, Mrs. Lee, who wrote the Memoirs of Baron Cuvier, with which you are probably acquainted. Mrs Lee intends to spend a few days to study the

33. RIDP. No. 106.
34. R. A. Smith, *Memoir of John Dalton (Manchester Memoirs 18, 1856)*, 264.

Ichthyology of the Lakes. I believe I met Mrs Lee at Baron Cuvier's; be this as it may, I feel great pleasure in being of any service to one who was so well acquainted with the Baron and with his most amiable daughter, from both of whom I received so many favours when in Paris in 1822, and since. Dr Holme and Dr Henry and family, of this place, are well acquainted with Mrs Lee.

Accept my kind remembrance, with best respects to Mrs Marshall and family.

Yours truly,
John Dalton.[34a]

LETTER 24 (To John Herschel)

Manchester, February 28th, 1833

Respected Friend,

Now that I have set pen to paper, I do not recollect whether I ever had an opportunity of returning you my thanks for the very excellent and scientific essay on sound which you did me the favour to send some time since. It is a subject that formerly engaged a good portion of my attention and for which I still feel much interest. The knowledge of this subject, perhaps more especially in this country, thirty years ago was not very extensively diffused. With regard to the propagation of sound in a mixture of gases (108) you assume as I have done (*Chemistry*, vol 1, page 186) that the atoms are arranged as in a perfectly quiescent atmosphere. Now this does not seem to be the fact; as far as I can find from recent experiments, they exist in *nearly* the same proportions at all accessible heights instead of the oxygen being the greatest proportion at the surface of the earth and less as we ascend. This arises, I judge, from the incessant agitation of the atmosphere, and the air from the top of

34a. Trinity College, Cambridge. Add. Mss. c 65 f 36. Addressed to "John Marshall, Esq., Hallsteads." Mrs. Sarah Lee (1791–1856) was first married to Thomas Bowdich, the African explorer, from whom she acquired her interest in natural knowledge. Among her many publications were *The Freshwater Fishes of Great Britain*, 1828, and *Memoirs of Baron Cuvier*, 1833. Marshall was a manufacturer, a founder of the Leeds "Phil. and Lit.," and had an estate by Ullswater.

the atmosphere at the equator coming down to the poles and often taking the lowest station: so that neither the azote nor oxygen atmospheres are ever in the quiescent position which theory presumes. This consideration may account for there being *one* sound from a distance instead of *two,* and perhaps may account for that one sound being lengthened somewhat like a clap of thunder, as Cavallo has observed. Being out in the country on a very fine calm day (the celebration of the Jubilee for King George the Third) I heard several firings of cannon from Liverpool (30 miles distant). These reports began softly, rose higher, and then died gradually, occupying as near as I could estimate from 1 to 2″ of time each.

Your explanation of thunder accords with the one which I have given for more than 20 years, and it is one which was with me an original, as I am not aware that a similar one had previously been published. I think it occurred to me about the year 1808. I gave a sketch of two clouds with a zigzag line betwixt them and, supposing the distance of the clouds from each other to be 10 or 12 miles, I imagined the discharge from one to the other to be made in a moment of time, and a spectator on the ground to be somewhere between the two extremes. This drawing with a corresponding explanation of the phenomena of thunder was given by me in a lecture on electricity at the Royal Institution, London, in January 1810. Davy highly approved of it, and repeated the explanation in one of his lectures soon after. The bursts and variations, I accounted for from the greater and less resistance the air makes to the passage from the successive parts being more dry or moist. I had a fine opportunity of verifying the theory a few years after. Being upon an elevated bowling green 2 miles N.W. of Manchester one afternoon, I observed a line of clouds spreading in a direction S.E. towards Stockport (distant 8 miles). On a sudden we were alarmed by a vivid flash of lightning succeeded almost instantaneously by loud thunder, which evidently seemed to begin with us and to proceed S.E. till it died away towards Stockport. No more thunder was heard, the clouds dispersed and the evening was clear and fine. My next door neighbour

happened to be at Stockport at that time. He told us on his return they had had a tremendous clap of thunder about 4
o'clock at Stockport, which alarmed the inhabitants much by
its proximity, being over the town and succeeding the lightning immediately, but he had not heard of any damage. Only
one clap was heard, and on a comparison it was found to have
occurred at the same time as with us.

I am most respectfully,

Yours, etc.,

John Dalton.[35]

LETTER 25 (To J. L. Gay-Lussac)

Manchester, August 5th, 1833

Respected Friend,

Major Emmett, a military officer of the Engineers, being
about to repair to Paris to spend a few weeks, and being desirous to improve the occasion by the acquisition of useful knowledge, more especially in the chemical and mechanical arts, to
which his genius as well as his profession seems to incline him,
has requested me to give him an introduction to one or two
persons who may be most able to facilitate his purpose. Major
E. has frequently attended the meetings of our Philosophical
Society, and has had some instructions from me in the theory
and practice of chemistry. He has travelled a good deal in his
military capacity, having been in North and South America,
West Indies, St. Helena, and various parts of Europe.

I should esteem it a favour if you would impart to him such
directions as the occasion may require and which can be given
without much inconvenience to yourself, engaged as I presume
you are with various and important concerns.

I remain with the greatest regard,

Yours truly,

John Dalton.[36]

35. BM. Add. Mss. 29,300, f. 49. Addressed to "Sir John F.W. Herschel." The references are to Dalton's own *New System of Chemical Philosophy*, and to T. Cavallo, *The Elements of Natural or Experimental Philosophy*, 4 vols. (1803).

36. Royal Society of London (hereafter referred to as RSL). Cat. no. MM I 7. The
letter is addressed to "M. Gay-Lussac, Member of the Institute, etc., Paris." An

P.S. Mr Hadfield, a friend of mine, having the care of a stove which is heated gradually every week from the common temperature up to 250° Fahrenheit, has at my suggestions made a number of experiments on the force and specific gravity of vapours from various liquids, as water, ether, alcohol, pyroxylic and pyroacetic spirits, acetic acid, etc.

His apparatus is similar to a thermometer tube, only indefinitely larger: the ball is 2 inches or more diameter, the tube 40 inches long and 2/10 inches diameter within. The capacities of both being determined, he fills them with mercury, inverts the instrument and then sends up, in a small bulb, a minute portion of liquid, which on reaching the summit of the column of mercury is liberated into the vacuum. The instrument then is attached to a graduated frame and exposed in the heated room along with a thermometer.

Water, ether, and alcohol he finds to agree nearly with your former experience. Pyroxylic spirit .810 specific gravity yields vapour of 1.28 specific gravity reduced to common temperature and pressure, but this probably is too high, on account of the impurity of the spirit. Pyroacetic spirit .868 specific gravity yields vapour about 2 specific gravity. Acetic acid yields vapour of 1.68 specific gravity nearly.

From my own analysis of these I find pyroxylic spirit atom (⊛), pyroacetic atom (⊛), acetic atom (⊛) or perhaps (⊛) as I formerly represented it (See my *Chemistry,* 1808).

LETTER 26 (To Major Emmett?)

Manchester, July 14th, 1835

Respected Friend,

I duly received the parcel you were so good as to send me, and what I felt most highly interested in was your remarks relative to the late dreadful catastrophe in the coal pit.

The explosions in coal mines are a subject which I have long

identical letter addressed to M. Biot, but without the postscript, is listed below. Anthony Emmett had a distinguished military career. See the *DNB.* For an 18 October 1833 paper by William Hadfield, see *Manchester Memoirs 11* (1842), 158–170.

had under consideration and am fully persuaded the accidents might often be foreseen and guarded against if due attention were paid. I presume it will be allowed that the pits do not get charged with fire damp in a moment, but that days and weeks are gradually adding to the charge. If so, any overlooker or other person might fill a small phial with the airs of the pit and send it up for examination. If the air was passed through an eudiometer filled with limewater, it would shew the *choke-damp* by the milkiness, if any amounting to 1 per cent were in it. And if 1 or more per cent of *firedamp* were there, nothing would be required but to put 10 or 15 per cent of pure hydrogen to the washed gas and, firing the mixture, the appearance of milkiness would clearly shew the existence of firedamp, and it would be no difficult matter next to find the *percentage* of that firedamp.

I have frequently found that no explosion takes place with pure firedamp in common air, unless it be between the limits of 1 to 7 and 1 to 13 of air.

I write this in haste having only had a few hours notice. I have not seen Mr Hadfield since I received yours. I believe he is well.

Yours truly,
John Dalton.[37]

LETTER 27 (To Major Emmett)

Manchester, December 15th, 1835

Dear Friend,

I was about to write you a week ago, before I received your interesting letter. I have had an instrument, a present from Mr H. H. Watson of Bolton for you, in my possession for a month or two, since which no opportunity of sending it safely occurred. It is Leslie's hygrometer improved. However he has sent for it again, thinking he can still improve the scale, so that on the whole it is better for the delay and, as you are contemplating a change of residence, it may remain here until you give directions respecting it.

37. RSL. Catalogue no. MM I 9. No address, but possibly to Major Emmett.

With respect to the inflammable gas of mines, I should be disposed to think it not infrequently collects *gradually and not in the manner you suggest:* but that can only be determined by experiments. I have never been so fortunate as to procure a sample of gas from a mine that contained any of the inflammable gas. By means of Mr Hadfield, however, I got a sample of gas in an ounce phial from the lowest level of the Worsley pits, and was surprised to find that though it had neither firedamp not chokedamp in it, yet it was deficient in oxygen, only yielding 17 or 18 per cent, instead of 21.

I was glad to hear of your going to Bermuda to reside because I think it is a promising opportunity to learn the particulars of the climate, the winds, tides, etc. I hope the Association will furnish you with the requisite instruments, etc. One thing I should be anxious to ascertain: whether the *carbonic acid* in the atmosphere is the same or not, compared with what we find at land in Europe. It has been stated to be less at sea than at land. I found plenty between Liverpool and Dublin. A glass vessel holding 2 or 3 quarts or more should be filled with water and then emptied, or if it was blown into by a pair of bellows, it would be as well. Then let an ounce, less or more, of lime water be poured in and the bottle be well corked. For two or three days it should be well agitated occasionally and at length the lime water poured out and tested carefully by some dilute acid, the lime water being also previously tested. Then the diminution of the lime in the lime water by the carbonic acid in the air will be found, and 19/24 or 5/6 of the weight of lime lost in the process will be the weight of the carbonic acid in a volume of air equal to that of the bottle. You may expect [one?] volume in 1000 or 1500.

With respect to the uses and observations of the thermometer and barometer, you must be too familiar to need any instruction. For a rain-gauge I use a funnel of 10 inches diameter with an upright rim of 3 inches, fixed into a wooden frame, with a bottle underneath to catch the rain. This is measured in a graduated bottle of 2 inches diameter and 8 or 10 inches deep, with a graduated scale for 10ths and hundredths of inches of water.

Should you wish for any other information on these or any other subjects I shall be happy if I can impart it.

I remain yours truly,

J. Dalton.[38]

LETTER 28 (To Major Emmett)

Manchester, February 13th, 1836

Dear Friend,

I received your letter and bottles of gas safely, and soon after opened the bottles under water. The air in each bottle was very much alike. It was constituted of some 2 or 3 per cent of carbonic acid, about 1/10 common air rather short of oxygen, and the rest, about 85 per cent was pure carburetted hydrogen or pond gas (o●o), without a trace of either pure hydrogen or olefiant gas.

The bottle of water from the old waste I also examined. It contained about 1 per cent of soluble matters, chiefly common salt with some carbonic acid, sulphurous acid, sulphuretted hydrogen and lime.

I thank you for your intelligence relative to the aurora of November 18th. You may not be apprised that on the same evening as well as on the 17th, the aurora was equally splendid and alarming in the United States of America. From Boston to Washington was one grand illumination. I think these unusually grand appearances are often followed by a disturbed state of the atmosphere, but the more singular ones seem to have little if any sensible effect on the weather.

I hope you will take out of a bottle of lime water by the sea air now and then for carbonic acid, with . . . [?] of it properly exposed. And at Bermuda you will have the finest opportunity for investigating the total quantity in that region. The phe-

38. RSL. Catalogue no. MM I 10. Addressed to "Major Emmett, Newcastle on Tyne." Dalton had sailed from Liverpool to Dublin for the meeting of the British Association for the Advancement of Science earlier in the year (see letter 29).

nomena of the tides will not be unworthy of your notice in that place.

I shall be glad to hear from you on these or other subjects after you have ascertained any local facts relative to them.

I remain, wishing you a prosperous voyage, and an agreeable residence in your new situation,

Yours truly,

John Dalton.[39]

LETTER 29 (To Hannah Tipping)

Manchester, 4th mo. 18th, 1836

Dear Cousins,

I write to inform you that we shall be glad to see one or both of you at 27 Falkner Street on the ensuing Quarterly Meeting. We shall have a bed at your service.

I had no time to call on our return from Dublin, as it was evening on our arrival at Liverpool, and we left next morning. We had a roughish passage to Dublin, but an extremely fine one on our return. About 60 or 70 sat down to dinner on the deck, with the sea as smooth as glass and a brilliant sunny even. We were highly delighted with the meeting of the Association and with our reception in Dublin.

I remain etc.,

J. Dalton.[40]

LETTER 30 (To Michael Faraday?)

Manchester, 29th of July, 1840

Dear Friend,

I sent up two papers on 1839 (I think it was in May) on the phosphates and the arseniates.

You delivered them the 20 of June, 1839, as I find by the *Philosophical Magazine,* Vol. 15, page 327, for which you have

39. **RSL**. Catalogue no. MM I 11. Addressed to "Major Emmett, Messrs. Cox and Co., Army Agents, Craigs Court, London."
40. EFS. Addressed to "Hannah Tipping, Great George Place, Liverpool."

my thanks. There were in all ten papers on various subjects read at the Society.

As I think it will not be published, there being several papers read since, in the *Philosophical Transactions,* I would thank [you] to take the trouble to send me down the articles of the *Phosphates* and the *Arseniates.* It follows as matter of course that they should be reclaimed by the author.

I have an imperfect copy of them, but I should wish to send the *originals,* as I have taken great pains with them.

I have the following essays by me:

"On the mixture of sulphate of magnesia and biphosphate of soda: no magnesia in it."

"On the *acid, base* and *water* in salts: they are united in atomic proportions; no ½ or ¼ or ⅛ parts of atoms of water that I have found as yet."

"On the *microcosmic salt.*"

It is my present intention to publish them together with the *Phosphates and Arseniates,* as a sequel to my *Chemistry.*

I am with great respect,

Yours faithfully,

John Dalton.[41]

LETTER 31 (To Michael Faraday)

September 3rd, 1840

Dear Friend Dr Faraday,

I have been from home more than a week in Cumberland, having Peter Clare with me and my servant man, partly on business and partly on pleasure and on account of my health.

I am sorry to find you are in the same predicament as to health. You have not been injured as to *lead,* as I was in London? Lead in *porter* and lead in *water* was my beverage. I was more than a year in getting rid of this complaint in 1804.

41. Royal Institution, London. No address, but presumably to Michael Faraday. Dalton published these other essays together with the pieces on the arseniates and phosphates. He added the petulant note of a lonely old invalid: "They were rejected [by the Royal Society]. Cavendish, Davy, Wollaston and Gilbert are no more." See A. L. Smyth, *John Dalton. A Bibliography of Works by and about Him* (Manchester, 1966), 6.

My recent attack of paralysis was from *extreme* cold. Being at York and Chester on trials, I was subject in *winter* to the extremity of *cold,* and being temperate and *regular* in my meals, I was subject to irregularities in present situation which were too much for me.

I shall be obliged to you for copies of my papers of *Phosphates* and *Arseniates,* at my expense. They are not long. I suppose 20 or 30 shillings will be the extremity. I want to publish them forthwith. I have copies, but *verbatim* I shall not say.

I observe the Council have voted the Rev. Mr Farquehasson's paper as fit for publication in the 2nd part of 1839. The height of the *aurora* was 1897 *yards,* or rather above 1 mile. I calculated it 100 to 160 miles (1828). Mr Cavendish 52 to 71 miles (1790), Robert Wise Fox, 1000 miles (1831). This would be an interesting phenomenon to the *British Association*— whether its height was 1 or 1000 miles.

I am your friend,
John Dalton.[42]

OTHER UNPUBLISHED LETTERS

In addition to the letters reproduced or referred to above, the manuscripts of a further twenty-one previously unknown letters have also been traced. These additional letters are not of sufficient interest to warrant publication but, in order to provide a complete record, brief details of their locations and contents are given in the following table.

Date	Recipient	Subject of letter	Location of ms.
23 Dec. 1792	John Robinson and George Bewley	Dispute with brother over father's will (2 pp.)	WHML

42. Royal Institution, London. No address given. Excerpt in Henry, *Memoirs of Dalton,* p. 22, where the controversy with Farquehasson is also discussed. This and the previous letter now also appear in L. P. Williams, ed., *The Selected Correspondence of Michael Faraday,* 2 vols (Cambridge, Cambridge University Press, 1971).

Date	Recipient	Subject of letter	Location of ms.
20 Sept. 1799	Jonathan Backhouse	Comparison of rainfall in Darlington, Kendal, and Manchester (1 p.)	The Prior's Kitchen, Durham University; Backhouse papers
23 March 1801	Jonathan Backhouse	Rainfall measurements; also Dalton's *English Grammar* (1 p.)	
29 March 1814	Edmund Sibson	Possibility of Sibson writing an essay on "moving force" (1 p.)	Warrington Public Library; Sibson papers
28 Dec. 1814	Mr Orchard	The paying off of an annuity (1 p.)	BM, Add. Mss. 37, 725, f.2
31 Oct. 1817	Paul Moon James	Accepts offer of accommodation while in Birmingham (1 p.)	LSF, Temp Mss. 10 a 19
14 April 1825	Paul Moon James	Sending portraits; anxious over boxes not yet received from Birmingham (2 pp.)	LSF, Temp Mss. 10 a 19
19 April 1825	John Hogg	Meteorological subjects (1 p.)	SML, Ms. no. 1954–357
4 July 1825	Edmund Sibson	Proposed visit by Dalton to Beaumaris, N. Wales (1 p.)	Warrington Public Library; Sibson papers
17 Aug. 1829	John Fletcher	Account of a Lake District walking holiday (2 pp.)	Fitz Park Museum, Keswick
10 June 1830	Cornelius Nicholson	Acknowledges election to Kendal Natural History and Scientific Society (1 p.)	Kendal Public Library
5 Aug. 1833	J. B. Biot	See letter 25 above	RSL, cat. no. MM I 8
28 March 1834	Thomas Thomson (Liverpool Quaker, not Glasgow chemist)	A collection of minerals which Thomson has for sale (1 p.)	LSF

Date	Recipient	Subject of letter	Location of ms.
29 July 1834	H. H. Watson	Note detailing recent journeys to the Lake District, etc. (½ p.)	MLPS
17 March 1837	T. E. Suliot	Possible dates for an interview (1 p.)	SML, Ms. no. 1954–358
14 Sept. 1838	Miss Wood	Account of the journey to Cockermouth (½ p.)	MLPS
20 May 1839	William Brockendon	Acknowledgment of drawing (1 p.)	National Portrait Gallery
14 Jan. 1841	C. G. B. Daubeny	Acknowledgment of Daubeny's *Supplement.* My memory is gone. Visit of Davies Gilbert (1 p.)	Magdalen College, Oxford. Mss. 400, item 88
12 April 1842	Hannah Abbatt	Dalton agreeable to her proposed stay with him (½ p.)	MLPS
No date	Not known	Recipient's paper to the Literary and Philosophical Society (½ p.)	MLPS
No date	Peter Ewart junior	Dalton's sale of a spare copy of Newton's *Principia* to Ewart senior (½ p.)	Durham University Library [43]

43. Durham University Library also possesses the copy of the *Principia.*

8. Bibliographic Essay

*If I have succeeded better than
many who surround me, it has been
chiefly, nay, I may say almost
solely from unwearied assiduity.*
       John Dalton in 1833

MANUSCRIPTS

This study has made use of new manuscript sources. Their nature, locations, and additional possibilities deserve some brief discussion.

Through the course of the nineteenth century, the Manchester Literary and Philosophical Society gradually became the major repository of Dalton documents, as explained in Chapter 3. The greater part of these documents perished with the Society's premises, in a 1940 air-raid. Those that survived were stored in a basement at Manchester University and lost from view for almost a quarter-century. This "lost" material included such precious items as the 1805 and 1807 lecture syllabuses reproduced in this work and the manuscript of Dalton's 1830 retrospective account. It also included a variety of items not printed here, but deserving further study, such as manuscripts of some of Dalton's lecture courses, several testimonials he wrote, and a considerable number of letters he received. All are preserved, and once again available to scholars, in the new premises of the Manchester Society.

Although the "Lit and Phil" was one obvious place to seek Dalton material, two other types of source proved particularly rewarding. One was those major institutional libraries in which manuscripts remorselessly accrete, the other those public and private archives in some way associated with one or other phase of

Dalton's career. Examples of the former are the British Museum, the Wellcome Historical Medical Library, the Edgar Fahs Smith Collection in the History of Chemistry, and the Gratz Collection of Scientific Autographs at the Historical Society of Pennsylvania. These four libraries between them produced a valuable sequence of thirteen letters, while occasional Dalton items turned up in other institutional collections as varied as the National Library of Scotland and Harvard University. Libraries directly connected with Dalton's career proved even less canvassed and more fruitful.

Most striking were the resources offered by that notably literate, conscientious, and record-prone group, the Society of Friends. Their disavowal of the legal and religious forms of English life made all the more urgent their own recording of members' marriages and progeny, while schools and education were matters dear to their hearts and familiar to their *Minutes*. The rich store of records now accumulated in the Kendal Meeting House (as smaller Meetings in the Lake District have one by one closed down) proved tremendously helpful on both the broader context and the detailed minutiae of Dalton's early life. Documents in the Mount Street Meeting, Manchester, offered similar, but less important, information on his later years. Manuscripts in the Library of the Society of Friends, London, threw light on many of his friends and acquaintance.

Manchester College, Oxford, possesses a variety of letters illuminating the concerns of the Manchester Academy it once was. Its early Minute Books detail Dalton's problems and progress as a professor. The Royal Society was another obvious and rewarding source. Material obtained at the Royal Institution illustrates a problem familiar to all researchers in British archives: uncatalogued and unsorted material. The manuscript *Managers' Minutes* of the Royal Institution show that Dalton was the first choice of their ad hoc "Committee of Science" when Thomas Young's 1803 resignation created an urgent need for replacement teaching (see Chapter 5, Note 17 above). The Minutes of the Committee are needed to establish the extent of their interest in Dalton (and his in them), and these Minutes may—or may not—

exist among still uncatalogued material at the Royal Institution.

One final type of archive proved both the most elusive and the most rewarding. It is the private family archive. The papers of the Dalton family were deposited at the Cumberland and Westmorland Record Office in 1965 and are now freely accessible. Papers of other local Quakers such as Thomas Wilkinson and Elihu Robinson are available at Carlisle Public Library. The Hodgkin papers (still in private hands) proved useful on John Gough's controversy with Dalton over mixed gases. If the manuscripts of such figures as Luke Howard, Thomas Percival, and Peter Ewart could be located, much fresh light would be thrown on John Dalton and late Hanoverian natural philosophy. It is tempting to regard such manuscripts as forever lost. The results of even this limited survey show how inimical to scholarship that assumption could be.

PRINTED WORKS

Study of Dalton's life and work has been enormously aided by the appearance of A. L. Smyth's *John Dalton. A Bibliography of Works by and about Him* (Manchester, Manchester University Press, 1966). Smyth's book is far more than just a bibliography. It details portraits, sculptures, and illustrations, as well as providing listings and brief descriptions of surviving (mainly Manchester) manuscripts known to its author. These listings are extensive but by no means exhaustive. Smyth also misses the occasional important paper about or by Dalton [for example, *Nicholson's Journal,* quarto series, 5 (1802), 241–244]. However, this bibliography is an indispensable reference work. Complementary to it, and providing a conspectus of recent scholarship, is D. S. L. Cardwell, ed., *John Dalton and the Progress of Science* (Manchester, Manchester University Press, 1968). The record of the 1966 bicentenary conference held in Manchester, it provides specialist articles on different aspects of Dalton's achievement. The focus is on the intellectual background to and consequences of the chemical atomic theory. The volume unfortunately fails to deal adequately with Dalton's life and thought. However, a great mass of material on these, spliced with rich and recondite bibliographical information is available in a third indispensable work, J. R. Partington's *A History of Chemistry*, III (MacMillan, 1962), ch. 17.

As unavoidable as it is unsatisfactory, the "official" life of Dalton is W. C. Henry's *Memoirs of the Life and Scientific Researches of John Dalton* (1854). It has been shamelessly pillaged by subsequent biographers, who have too often taken its uncritically assembled anecdotes of Dalton's later years as historically reliable information. A study of Henry's work reveals that 24.2 percent of its contents is direct quotation of memories and hearsay evidence, of little worth (for examples, see Chapters 2 and 3 above). Of more use is the 21.1 percent occupied with reproduction of contemporary printed and manuscript evidence, some of which is now lost or destroyed. Even this information must be treated with reserve, because of the author's habit of editing, conflating, and suppressing sections of his source material, without indication or explanation.

R. A. Smith's 1856 *Memoir of John Dalton and History of the Atomic Theory up to His Time* (*Manchester Memoirs* 18) adds little concerning Dalton's life, but is useful for affording a mid-nineteenth century British view of the past course, present state, and future prospects of atomic theory. Far more informative on his life, though less so on his work, is Henry Lonsdale's *John Dalton,* The Worthies of Cumberland, no. 5 (1874). Himself a Cumberland Quaker, Lonsdale made sense of Dalton's background and early years in a way that escaped Henry and Smith. He also introduced a few additional manuscript sources, without greatly disturbing the pattern laid down by Henry. Regrettably, Lonsdale too preferred invoking the loss of evidence in the mists of time to searching those Quaker archives he was so well placed to exploit. His study thus offers a portrait of Dalton more important for its greater sympathy than its increased accuracy. The last of the Victorian biographies was H. E. Roscoe's avowedly popular

John Dalton and the Rise of Modern Chemistry, The Century Science Series (1895). This too introduced a few fresh dribs and drabs of source material, but is principally of interest as a thoroughgoing attempt to paint Dalton as the first of the Manchester school of chemistry. J. P. Millington's *John Dalton,* English Men of Science (Dent, 1906) is totally derivative and uninspired.

The meeting of the British Medical Association in the city was the occasion for a booklet by the Manchester physician and local historian, E. M. Brockbank, on *John Dalton. Experimental Physiologist and Would-be Physician* (Manchester, Falkner, 1929). The detail on Dalton's unfulfilled wish to study at Edinburgh was amplified in Brockbank's later volume *John Dalton. Some Unpublished Letters of Personal and Scientific Interest with Additional Information about his Colour-vision and Atomic Theories* (Manchester, Manchester University Press, 1944). Two recent popular biographies ably review and synthesize the material available in these diverse sources, while also making some reference to surviving manuscripts. Frank Greenaway's *John Dalton and the Atom* (Heinemann, 1966) was published on Dalton's 200th birthday, while Elizabeth Patterson's later *John Dalton and the Atomic Theory: The Biography of a Natural Philosopher* (New York, Doubleday, 1970) was able to draw on the insights of the bicentenary conference.

The serious student of Dalton's life and work must also consult a variety of other sources. Among these pride of place goes to H. E. Roscoe's and A. Harden's invaluable *New View of the Origin of Dalton's Atomic Theory. A Contribution to Chemical History. Together With Letters and Documents Concerning the Life and Labour of John Dalton, Now for the First Time Published from the Manuscript . . .* (1896, reissued by Johnson Reprint Co., New York, 1970). Here one may find copious extracts from the laboratory notebooks for the crucial years from 1802 to 1808, extracts all the more precious now the notebooks themselves have perished. Long sections from Dalton's 1811 Royal Institution lectures, and a variety of strategic letters, add to the enduring value of the work. It should be remembered that the editors consciously exercised their right of selection, without necessarily reporting their deliberate omissions.

In the same way that Roscoe and Harden provide the essential guide to Dalton's research notebooks, his public lectures can be followed in some detail in W. W. H. Gee, H. F. Coward and A. Harden, "John Dalton's Lectures and Lecture Illustrations," *Manchester Memoirs* 59 (1914–1915), no. 12 (66 pp., illus.). A further study of particular significance is T. T. Wilkinson's "Account of the Early Mathematical and Philosophical Writings of the Late Dr. Dalton," *Manchester Memoirs* *17* (1855), 1–30. Much may be gleaned from the various obituary notices recorded in Smyth's *Bibliography* cited above. Particularly informative are those in the *Annual Monitor of the Society of Friends 3* (1845), 40–47; *The Proceedings of the Royal Philosophical Society of Glasgow 2* (1844–1848), 79–88 (by Thomas Thomson); and *British Quarterly Review, 1* (1845), 157–198 (by George Wilson). Also worth mention is Sir David Brewster's slightly later "Memoirs of John Dalton," *North British Review* 27 (1857), 465–497. A recent essay with new information on his religious life in Manchester is J. T. Marsh's "Old Quaker Dalton," *Manchester Memoirs 111* (1969), 27–47.

The information readily available in local histories has been almost systematically ignored, with a consequent impoverishment of Dalton studies. For instance, much light on late-eighteenth century Kendal, including its Quaker school, is available in J. F. Curwen, *Kirbie-Kendall* (Kendal, Wilson, 1900). Also significant are F. Nicholson and A. Axon, *The Older Nonconformity in Kendal* (Kendal, Wilson, 1915); M. Irwin, *The History of the Pardshaw Meeting and Meeting House* (Friends Bookshop, 1919); B. Bonsall, *Sir James Lowther and the Cumberland and Westmorland Elections, 1754–1775* (Manchester, Manchester University Press, 1960); and E. Hughes, *Cumberland and Westmorland, 1700–1830*, North Country Life in the Eighteenth Century, no. 2 (Oxford University Press, 1965). Contemporary accounts of Dalton's life in Manchester are available in J. Wheeler, *Manches-*

ter. Its Political, Social and Commercial History (Manchester, 1836: autobiographical sketch) and [Anon], *Manchester As It Is. Or Notices of the Institutions . . . Of the Metropolis of Manufactures* (Manchester, 1839). Important for the intellectual life of the city itself is A. Prentice, *Historical Sketches and Personal Recollections of Manchester. Intended to Illustrate the Progress of Public Opinion from 1792 to 1832* (Manchester, 1857).

There is a further type of printed source, as yet unexploited. It consists of the copious volumes devoted to those many of his friends and acquaintance equipped with devoted daughters or other memorialists. For instance, Dalton features in E. H. Coleridge, ed., *Letters of Samuel Taylor Coleridge*, 1895; G. P. Fisher, *The Life of Benjamin Silliman*, 2 vols. (Philadelphia, 1866); A. Geikie, *The Life of Sir Roderick I. Murchison*, 2 vols. (1875); and [Anon], *Life of William Allen*, 3 vols. (1846), besides more obvious works devoted to Humphry Davy, Thomas Young, and so on. Biographical memoirs of local rather than cosmopolitan men of science are more obscure and correspondingly less consulted, but not therefore less rewarding. The *Biographical Memoir of Thomas Turner . . . By a Relative* (1875) and W. C. Williamson's *Reminiscences of a Yorkshire Naturalist* (1896) deserve particular mention.

The aspect of Dalton's work that has always attracted most attention is, of course, his chemical atomic theory. In addition to works already cited, A. N. Meldrum's *Avogadro and Dalton. The Standing in Chemistry of Their Hypotheses* (Edinburgh, Clay, 1906) should be consulted, as well as his series of studies on "The Development of Atomic Theory" in *Manchester Memoirs 54* (1909–1910), no. 7 (16 pp.); 55 (1910–1911), no. 3 (12 pp.); no. 4 (15 pp.); no. 5 (22 pp.); no. 6 (18 pp.); no. 19 (10 pp.); no. 22 (11 pp.). Recent debate may be followed in L. K. Nash, "The Origin of Dalton's Chemical Atomic Theory," *Isis 47* (1956), 101–116; F. Greenaway, "The Biographical Approach to John Dalton," *Manchester Memoirs 100* (1958–1959), 1–98; T. S. Wheeler and J. R. Partington, *The Life and Work of William Higgins* (Pergamon, 1960); H. E. Guerlac, "Some Daltonian Doubts," *Isis 52*

(1961), 544–554; R. Siegfried, "Further Daltonian Doubts," *Isis* 54 (1963), 480–481; A. Thackray, "The Origin of Dalton's Chemical Atomic Theory: Daltonian Doubts Resolved," *Isis* 57 (1966), 35–54; S. Mauskopf, "Thomson before Dalton," *Annals of Science* 25 (1969), 229–242, and "Daltonian Doubts Exhumed," *Ambix* 17 (1970), 182–191.

A number of studies deal with atomic theory in wider perspective. The eighteenth century background is explored in A. Thackray, *Atoms and Powers. An Essay on Newtonian Matter-Theory and the Development of Chemistry* (Cambridge, Mass., Harvard University Press, 1970). One particular episode in nineteenth century British thought is treated in W. H. Brock, ed., *The Atomic Debates. Brodie and the Rejection of Atomic Theory* (Leicester, Leicester University Press, 1967), while more extended developments are discussed in D. M. Knight's *Atoms and Elements. Theories of Matter in England in the Nineteenth Century* (Hutchinson, 1967). These same developments are placed in European perspective in W. V. Farrar's "Nineteenth Century Speculations on the Complexity of the Chemical Elements," *British Journal for the History of Science* 2 (1965), 247–323. R. Fox's *The Caloric Theory of Gases. From Lavoisier to Regnault* (Oxford, Clarendon Press, 1971) was published too late for use in the body of this work, but is important on Dalton's ideas about heat and the physics of gases. Finally, mention should be made of two books which seek to base broader generalizations about scientific thought in part of Dalton's work. The chemical atomic theory is one of the theories analyzed in J. B. Conant, ed., *Harvard Case Histories in Experimental Science*, 2 vols. (Cambridge, Mass., Harvard University Press, 1957). It also features extensively in T. S. Kuhn's brilliant and controversial analysis of *The Structure of Scientific Revolutions*, 2nd ed. (Chicago, Ill., University of Chicago Press, 1970).

Among works which deal with the broader intellectual content of natural philosophy at this period, several are especially helpful. Though now somewhat dated, A. Ferguson, ed., *Natural Philosophy through the Eighteenth Century* (1948, bicentenary issue of the *Philosophical Magazine*), is a useful guide. So too is A. Wolf, *A History of Science, Technology and Philosophy in the Eighteenth Century*, 2nd ed. (MacMillan, 1952). The pioneering exploration of Newtonian natural philosophy, to which all subsequent work remains indebted, is I. B. Cohen's monumental *Franklin and Newton* (*Memoirs of the American Philosophical Society 43*, Philadelphia, 1956) which also offers many important insights into the life of science in the period and contains an extensive bibliography. New perspectives appear in A. E. Musson and E. Robinson, *Science and Technology in the Industrial Revolution* (Manchester, Manchester University Press, 1969), and R. E. Schofield, *Mechanism and Materialism. British Natural Philosophy in an Age of Reason* (Princeton, N.J., Princeton University Press, 1970). For a slightly later period there are two particularly valuable studies. Its title accurately displays the concerns if not the subtlety of C. C. Gillispie's *Genesis and Geology. Scientific Thought, Natural Theology and Social Opinions in Great Britain, 1790–1850,* Harvard Historical Studies, *58* (Cambridge, Mass., Harvard University Press, 1951). W. F. Cannon, "History in Depth: The Early Victorian Period," *History of Science 3* (1964), 20–38, exposes the inadequacy of conventional stereotypes and outlines alternative analytical schemes. J. T. Merz, *A History of European Thought in the Nineteenth Century*, I (Blackwood, 1904), is of enduring value and is now nicely complemented by J. B. Morrell's stimulating survey of "Individualism and the Structure of British Science in 1830," *Historical Studies in The Physical Sciences 3* (1971), 183–204.

A variety of aspects of Dalton's life and work can only be adequately understood with the aid of other specialist and general studies. Among the former are A. Raistrick, *Quakers in Science and Industry. Being an Account of the Quaker Contributions to Science and Industry During the Seventeenth and Eighteenth Centuries* (Bannisdale, 1950); and N. Hans, *New Trends in Education in the Eighteenth Century* (Routledge and Kegan Paul, 1951); and two books concerning Manchester: A. Briggs, *Victorian Cities* (Odhams, 1963); and W. H. Thomson, *History of*

Manchester to 1852 (Altrincham, Sherratt, 1967). Useful general studies include J. Ben-David, *The Scientist's Role in Society* (Englewood Cliffs, N.J., Prentice Hall, 1971); W. E. H. Lecky, *A History of England in the Eighteenth Century*, 8 vols. (1878–1890); E. Halévy, *History of the English People in the Nineteenth Century*, 2nd ed., 6 vols. (Benn, 1949–1952); A. Briggs, *The Age of Improvement. 1783–1867* (Longmans, 1959); E. Hobsbawm, *The Age of Revolution. 1789–1848* (Weidenfeld and Nicholson, 1962); P. Deane, *The First Industrial Revolution* (Cambridge, Cambridge University Press, 1965); and P. Mathias, *The First Industrial Nation. An Economic History of Britain. 1700–1914* (Methuen, 1969).

Name Index

Subject Index

Absorption of gases, 72, 73, 81, 90, 100, 108, 111
American Philosophical Society, 148, 150
Annals de Chimie, 93
Annals of Philosophy, 92, 93
Apparatus, Dalton's, 17, 33, 44, 47, 48, 53, 57, 66, 67, 81, 107, 130, 131, 133, 139, 159
Arcueil, Society of, 55, 92
Atmosphere, 70, 71, 72, 82, 105, 109, 111, 163, 168, 169
Atomic models, 76, 96, 115, 117, 118, 120, 121, 122, 124
Atomic volumes, 93
Atomic weight, 34, 36, 87, 90, 92, 94-95, 115
Atoms, 62, 90, 113; simple atoms, 94-95, 100; double atoms, 94-95; compound atoms, 100

Birmingham, 57, 146, 159 and n
Botany, 46, 130, 131, 136, 137, 138
British Association for the Advancement of Science, 12, 20, 23, 35, 55-56, 56n, 115, 116, 117, 121, 162, 170, 172

Carbon compounds, 81, 87, 108, 110, 114, 169
Cavendish Society, 30 and n
Charles's Law of gases, 52, 70, 126
Chemical affinity, 71, 72, 73, 75

Chemical atomic theory, 24, 27, 40, 52, 61, 71, 79, 87, 149
Chemical combination, 36, 62, 76, 78, 80, 81, 85, 101, 108, 114, 124
Chemical compounds, 76, 87, 96, 98-99, 110, 114, 117, 118
Chemical elements, 81, 85, 95, 108, 112, 113
Chemical equivalents, 40, 63, 93, 94, 97, 98, 115
Chemical notation, 95-97, 115-117, 120-124
Chemical proportions, 28, 36, 62, 76, 79, 83, 92, 97-100, 114, 115
Chetham's Library, 15, 48
Coalbrookdale, 17, 145
Color blindness, 51, 130
Complex molecules, 120, 122. *See also* Organic compounds
Cumberland Pacquet, 19, 132, 140

Density of water, 80, 84, 146-147
Dew point, 69
Dissenters, 23, 26, 42, 51
Dublin, 121, 168, 170

Eaglesfield, 15, 18, 43, 128
Edinburgh, 3, 22, 23, 47, 56, 65, 84, 85, 112, 149, 151
Elastic fluids, 69, 85, 106, 107, 108
Evaporation, 68, 70, 111, 113

French *Académie,* 19, 20, 23, 55
Fitz Park Museum, Keswick, 132n, 138n